HENRY'S WORLD

A Three-Legged Cat's View of Human Absurdity

AN E-MAIL ODYSSEY

Cathy Conheim,
Cat Scribe

 Henry jm

Dr. Mom

Mom Cathy

Henry jm

Dolly, the prancing "horse"

Cat Scribe: Cathy Conheim
Photography and concept by Cathy Conheim
Design, layout, and photo captions by Timothy W. Brittain (twbrit@cox.net)
Additional photo captions by Cathy Conheim
Preliminary text editing and organizing by Marianne Gerdes
Additional photography by Henry's Friends and "Uncle" Tim Brittain
Henry's Web site designed by Kim Beecroft, www.pinkrobot.com

HENRY'S WORLD

ISBN 0-9679576-1-3
First Edition, September 2005
Second Edition, December 2005
Printed in Korea (sales@onlineprintings.com)

BREAKTHROUGH PRESS
P. O. Box 135
La Jolla, California 92038

To order:
www.henrysworld.org • www.breakthroughpress.com
or fill out a coupon in the back of book and send it to us.

Thanks for buying my book and helping my friends! How about a hug?

Dedication

To Chrissy,
— Because she insisted that Henry's adventures become a book

To Emmy Lu's Mom, Dee
— For her fighting spirit, courage, and love for animals

To Dr. Mom,
— Forever a healer, for rescuing Henry and keeping him

To all the dogs and cats of the world who grace us with their presence,

A heartfelt thank you!

Henry's endorsements from some of his fans:

Henry's story is one of the classic tales of love between human beings and the animal world. Like all such stories it is a moral tale of how much we learn and grow with one another. You don't even need to read! Henry tell his own story through the illustrations.

— Jill Ker Conway, President Smith College 1975–85, author

If cats really do have nine lives, then Henry's next eight lives have a really tough act to follow. He is only one year old and already he has survived a near fatal encounter with a car, converted a pair of life-long dog lovers, touched the hearts and minds of hundreds of people, and authored his own book! Henry really IS the cat's meow!

—BJ Gallagher, author of *A Peacock in the Land of Penguins* and human companion to Henry's tripod feline friend, Punkie

I've been faithful to dogs all my life and never thought a little cat could turn my head. But Henry isn't a little cat. He's a giant hero, and his story is an epic inspiration.

— Lillian Faderman, author and Professor of English

Henry and his scribe, therapist Cathy Conheim, have given each of us a new way to discover our own stories. By speaking to and through our animals, we free ourselves of the false and shallow masks we think we need for human interaction, and speak from our hearts. This book is a gift of comfort, joy and self-discovery.

— Heather Wood Ion, Managing Director/CEO Goldie Hawn's Bright Light Foundation. President, Wisdom Legacy

Cats don't usually talk, but we all have wondered what their inscrutable gaze would say. With the help of his cat scribe, Henry does talk. He infuses his inspirational wisdom into all of us. He humanizes the insurmountable. His story is everybody's story about people and their indominatability in making life work for them.

— Erv Polster, Ph.D., author/Gestalt Therapist

To enter Henry's World *is to share the special covenant between an extraordinary cat, his canine sister and his human staff. By the end of page one, I was an avid fan!*

— Marcia E. Brown, author

"Henry's World" is the perfect book for all who love animals. Henry's is a voice of conscience, compassion, unquenchable humor, and living each moment to its fullest no matter what life throws at us!

— David A. Naumann, Ph.D.

Dear Henry,
Your book is as much a purrfect delight as you are in person. Readers of all ages – even DOG persons like me – find your story moving and the pictures wonderful. Thanks for being you.

— Dr. Phyllis Irwin, Professor Emerita of Music, CSU Fresno

Henry's World *provides the perfect virtual pet for lonely seniors who have had to give up life friends in order to enter long-term care facilities. Those with dementia are engaged by the bright and vivid photographs, other seniors become enraptured by the amazing stories shared in the book's pages. Ultimately I hope that this may become a vehicle for uniting lonely elders through cyberspace.*

— Wendy Stein, M.D., CMD President/CEO Wendy Stein M.D. + Assoc.

Henry jm is destined to be famous, the Lassie of the feline world – he writes beautifully, he's observant, curious, empathic! And his Cat Scribe isn't bad either! Give yourself and your family a treat. Add this book to your library!

— Bob Wendlinger, author Ph.D.

What a cat! Even if you think you don't like cats, this one will wrap his paws around your heart and won't let go. Henry looks at life through the clear lens of a realist – an optimistic realist. He serves as an inspiration for those who face the world from a less than ideal viewpoint. In all my previous lives – youth correctional administrator, college dean, college president, vice president of a foundation dealing with youth in foster care, working as a civil rights advocate, and serving on boards of nonprofit organizations – I've dealt with those who could benefit from Henry's wise insights about how to navigate the hurdles of life. His story is an inspiration, and I am happy to endorse him as a good, and warm, fuzzy therapist.

— Katherine Gabel, Ph.D., J.D.

FOREWORD

THE BEGINNING

In the autumn of 2003 the worst fire ever to hit the state of California spread over 60 miles in the foothills and mountains east of San Diego. The fire caused massive destruction to homes, people, and habitat. The hills were blackened and covered with ash. The trees were transformed into skeleton-like forms. Everyone was sad and they slowly tried to clean up, rebuild, and tend to the living things left in the forest and mountains.

The fire threatened a little mining town in the mountains east of San Diego called Julian. The four-block historic mining town that dates back to the 1800s is where hundreds of firemen made a stand to save the town. They saved it, but at great expense to the rest of the area. Over 1200 homes were lost, untold numbers of wildlife destroyed, and well over half the forests burned. In one particular mile-long section of street only five homes remained. As I looked at all the destruction it was hard to understand how those five homes escaped total destruction, but they did. And one of them was ours. It was to become a refuge for many people and animals over the next 15 months.

A year later, in another part of Julian, a litter of four kittens was born. Who the parents were and what those kittens' first seven weeks were like we will never know. This story starts when they made their way to the lane that had been so badly burned and to the house that had been saved from the fire. It now became home to a litter of cats in addition to several people who had lost so much in the fire of 2003.

We not only had the incredible good fortune of having our home saved, but, since the fire, we also had a wonderful man and his family who came to live with us and help take care of the four acres and the house. I suppose, being 61 and 72 years of age, we fall into the category of older people. We can no longer do the physical activities to care for the property we have.

The caretaker of our home has two daughters. The older one wanted a kitty and we said, of course, she could have one. Although this is our second home, allowing cats on the property was a stretch. We are big-time DOG people. Together we have 131 years collective experience with DOGS. A cat had not yet crossed our path in the many years we had lived. Since it was to be the little girl's pet, and there was plenty of room, we saw no problem with having a kitty on the property. The next thing we knew there were four kittens scampering around the grounds. They lived outdoors and had no names; the little girl called them Kitty, Kitty, Kitty, and Kitty.

If the truth were known, we are people who treat animals with even more respect than humans. Animals are family members with all the house rights and privileges of family. Seeing these little kittens outside fending for themselves made us worry they would freeze, get killed, or meet some other tragic fate. Older people worry more than little girls.

So that is where the story of *Henry's World* began, in a town that had suffered immeasurable loss, and with Moms who were dealing with a loss of their own. At first, his presence (he being the only male in the feline quartet) was a welcome distraction from our personal anguish. Then, as his adventures unfolded day by day, I began sharing them with a circle of close friends. It wasn't long before Henry's stories developed a devoted following. It was clear there was something bigger than Henry and his world that kept us hooked.

Henry's stories are similar to *The Velveteen Rabbit*. They are stories about essence as opposed to form. They are about unlikely bedfellows, about prejudice being softened by chance exposure. They are about spirit and spunk, about being yourself in a world that invites you to be everybody but yourself. Little Henry reaches deeply into all sorts of hearts. He is about how we survive our wounds. He reminds us that it is not the events of our lives, but our responses to them, that dictate what happens to us. Henry's life is about reframing tragedy into possibility, about random acts of kindness, and about getting more back than you put out. It is about trust when there seems to be no good reason to do so. Just as *The Velveteen Rabbit* taught us that being real was about being loved, love and caring are what makes us all real. In the end, we are not our positions or our possessions. In the end there is just love.

Henry's World is more than a story about a cat. It is a story about all of us, about trust, community, courage and resiliency. It is a story about prejudice and overcoming it, coming to love what we thought we hated, enemies becoming friends, challenges becoming learning experiences and, foremost, that life is a series of adventures.

I grew up in a world where animals were what I knew and trusted. I always talked for my dogs and through my dogs. My most beloved books were books about animals. Author Kenneth Grahame's *Wind and the Willows* is one of my favorites. I understood intimately the archetypes each of those animals represented. In the foreword it is written that this is the kind of book you give to your intended, and if he or she doesn't like it, you cancel the engagement. The book seems to say more about who the reader is than anything else.

Animals were my first and deepest connection. I have always had them in my life. I have been a psychotherapist for over 30 years now. My work is my privilege and passion and the most interesting thing I can imagine doing. But outside of that world,

I always return to the world of animals, particularly dogs. I don't know if I will ever let a cat into my heart as deeply as a dog, but if there is ever a spirit animal who could challenge that barrier, it is Henry.

Henry's being, in a virtual way, was born of the Internet, and will continue in that realm. I didn't write this book. In the strangest of ways, Henry did. He had only one front paw, so he asked for my assistance with the typing part. It appears that I can now add "Cat Scribe" to my résumé. Welcome to *Henry's World*!

— *Cathy Conheim*
February 2005

The first edition of Henry's book came out in late September 2005. As we approach Christmas, to his owners' amazement, he has had five articles written about him and in February 2006 he and Mom Cathy are going to be on the cover of *San Diego Pets Magazine*.

He has made wonderful new friends in this year and his paw pal list grows daily. His journey has truly become a heart journey and Henry has a heart big enough to love all who come into his world. He has been 100% successful in winning the hearts and souls of his two dog-devoted Moms.

— *Cathy Conheim*
Christmas 2005

"Sorry, Henry, but we couldn't put all of your friends' messages in here!"

(paws)

"Mee-OW!"

1—THE HUMAN ELEMENT

A Strange Thing Happened on the Way to Julian

Date: Saturday, November 6
From: Cathy C. • To: All My Friends

The last weeks have been a struggle.

So much loss. I felt like I'd been hit by a car and some part of me got severed. And then, a very strange thing happened yesterday. As you know we are dog people. I never had a cat nor have I ever wanted one, especially with a dog.

The caretaker of our property, a lovely Hispanic man, has a nine-year-old daughter who took on four abandoned kittens, now four months old. I worried about them because they were outside and not even named. In the Hispanic culture, as far as animals are concerned, they believe in the wisdom of nature. It is survival of the fittest. I am an animal nut and that was not OK with me. So I bought an insulated little place for them to sleep in, tuna fish and canned food and milk to eat, and went to look out for the kitties every weekend. Last week we decided to give them names, as the little girl had named them all "Kitty." We discovered there were three girls and a boy. The boy became Henry, and the girls had other, softer names.

Henry was a bold little kitty. His first time in the house ever, he walked right up to our dog Dolly and put his little nose to hers. It was a tense thirty seconds, and then he rubbed against her paws and started to purr. Dolly didn't attack. She was curious and at one point they lay down on the couch together. I was relieved, but not sure we would risk it again, as Dolly, even in playing, could really hurt the kitty.

We went up to Julian yesterday and three out of the four kitties came running up. No Henry. I asked where Henry was, and the little girl said he was in his house. She thought he broke his leg. We ran to get Henry and saw immediately that he had had some sort of accident. His front paw was just dangling. The nerve was cut so he was in no pain. His eyes told us there was a concussion. We put Dolly in the house and drove to the country vet with Henry. He was affectionate and purring on his first car ride. As I looked at him I saw myself; very wounded but still available for life and love.

The vet confirmed that the front leg would have to be amputated

at the shoulder. This meant he could no longer be an outdoor cat. It would be very expensive. First they would treat the concussion and then, if he's all right, amputate on Monday or Tuesday. We sat in the car with Henry looking trustingly into our eyes. We finally decided that we had no home for him so we would have to put him to sleep. Neither of us could do it. We went back in to get the tests started.

At the same time, there was a woman and her daughter in the office who took one look at Henry and fell in love. The woman had just had her beloved cat put to sleep the week before. If we paid for the surgery, she was willing to take him, but she had to ask her husband. We took her phone number, felt incredibly lucky, and told the vet to proceed with treatment. We would pay the bill.

We went back to visit Henry. The vet tech had fallen in love with his sweet nature. When we saw him, Henry immediately ran to me and got in my lap and just stared into my eyes. He spent the next hour in our laps, looking at us, cuddling up, and finding his way into our hearts.

There was something strange about this wounded animal. He was so full of life and love and so trusting when the world had practically killed him. We went on some errands and came back because the tech said she was going to give him his first bath. Cats hate water. Henry just lay down and purred during his first bath. When we returned he was clean for the first time in his four months. He limped to me and jumped back into my lap, his front paw dangling. I swear Henry was saying "I am here to remind you that you can't give up no matter how bad you are hurt. They can cut you off at the knees but you have to crawl back. Love, in the end, will win."

So against all our logical energy, we went to get Henry after the amputation and brought the little tripod home to live with us. The woman who wanted him was disappointed but we said we were going to try it post-operatively and see how it worked because we had never had a cat and we already had a dog. She said if it didn't work out she would take Henry.

It was all incredibly unlikely but I felt part of a weight lift and got back a little of my spirit. We are still wounded deeply, but Henry's arrival has reminded us we must reach out to each other with love.

By the way, there is one of Henry's sisters that is up for the taking, no amputation but very cute. Let us know if you want a sweet, pretty little girl and we will send you a picture. Take care and know that we love you all. Tomorrow Donna will be 71. She said "I want that cat," so I guess Henry is her birthday present.

– *Love, Cathy, along with Donna, Dolly, and Henry*

Subject: Tripods
Date: Saturday, November 7
From: Maryanne C. • To: Cathy

What a wonderful story about Henry. As it happens, we have a few three-legged pooches in our neighborhood. One, a mutt named Skipper, lives the life of Riley in an elegant town house with devoted humans. Another, a handsome and loving black pit bull named Hopper (really), belongs to the sister of a friend of mine who is a vet. There are two others that I see occasionally with their owners, but I don't know their names. One is a beagle with a missing hind paw and the other is a small fluffy dog with a missing front leg. They all seem happily unaware of their handicaps. City life is hazardous for animals. Seems country life is, too.

— Love, Maryanne

Date: Saturday, November 5
From: Cathy C. • To: Maryanne

That is encouraging to hear about the three-legged creatures. We have renamed Henry Tripod, in honor of his upcoming surgery, or TP for short. His surgery should be Monday or Tuesday. He is responding very well to his meds for the concussion. I look around our house, which has much stained glass and glass sculptures, and go — **gulp!** *It is neither kid- nor cat-proof. Oh well, we shall see. He seems to have been sent our way. As I have never had a cat in six decades plus, I know not a thing.*

— Cathy

Date: Saturday, November 6 • From: River M. • To: Cathy

Dear Cathy,

You are such a wonderful storyteller and this is such a wonderful story about such a wonderful cat. I find loving cats AND dogs really GREAT. Especially sleeping with cats. What a wonderful lesson in resilience.

— Love, River

Date: Sunday, November 7
From: Maryanne • To: Cathy

I think Henry is a nicer name — why define him by his handicap? If you don't want to lose all your glass and pottery, get some modeling clay (the kind we used to play with as kids) and put a good-sized dab of it on the bottom of every vase and sculpture. It will anchor the piece without damaging it. That's what many of my friends do. The little guy probably won't get into as much trouble as a four-legged cat, but you never know. Get him a scratching post to discourage him from sharpening his claws on your furniture. Cats are not nearly as trainable as dogs, and you have to accept that going in. They are wonderful in their own way, but they are NOT dogs.

— Maryanne

Date: Sunday, 07 Nov 2004
From: Heile
To: Henry

Dear Henry,

You don't know me but I am a survivor too, and a cat lover.

I cried when I read of your fate but then I realized you were in the hands of professional animal caretakers and the best animal lovers in the whole world. You will have a great and exciting life, live in a very beautiful home (I call it a castle) and take weekend trips to your retreat in the mountains. Dolly will watch over you and give you lessons in living. My caretaker is leaving tomorrow for Kauai so I am a little sad today, but it's only for 8 days. Know that we all love you. May I call you "dangle toes"?

— Your friend, Heile

It's Been a Long Road

Date: Wednesday, November 10
From: Henry • To: Everyone

Dear New Friends,

As all of you know, Dr. Mom and Mom Cathy are still feeling really sad. It has been a hard time for them. It wasn't a very good week for me either. I am only four months old and my whole life had been scampering outdoors in chilly, beautiful Julian. I got a name last week, which made me very proud. My three sisters and I played a lot and slept on top of each other. It was a hard life but I was not an unhappy boy.

Then my world changed. I am not entirely sure what happened. I got broadsided by something way bigger than me and then I couldn't feel my front leg any more. The little girl in Julian who cared for me put me in the tiny house that Mom Cathy got us and I stayed there for a day or two. Then Mom Cathy and Dr. Mom came up. They took one look at me and zap, I was in a red van going somewhere called a vet hospital. I never saw trees move so fast. I thought all trees stood still like the ones my sisters and I climbed.

For a while all the trees went by and then next I knew I was on a table with people poking me and looking at me. I didn't understand much of what they were saying, but it had something to do with whether I was going to be "put to sleep." Mom Cathy cried a lot, so I guess she doesn't like sleeping. My Moms took me to their car to "make a decision." They said I couldn't be an outdoor cat anymore if I had something called an

"We can't get attached to him because we can't keep him. We're <u>dog</u> people."

amputation. I just lay on Dr. Mom's lap and purred and looked deeply into each of their souls. I knew we were meant to be together, but they weren't so sure. I could tell they weren't cat people. I knew they were feeling troubled about something. I hoped they would open their hearts and give me a chance to help them feel better about cats, and whatever else it was that was troubling them.

Finally, we went back into the building and there another lady and her daughter fell in love with me. They said if Cathy and Donna paid for the operation (whatever *that* is) they would take me. The problem was that I didn't want to be taken. I wanted to stay with my Moms. After all, I'd gone through a lot to get where I am.

I think it was the way I stared into their eyes that did it. They decided I would have my operation, I would become a three legged kitty , and, I would get to tame Dolly and live with them in their permanent home.

Dr. Mom thinks I am her birthday present. She says I am really a symbol of hope against all odds.

I think hope is a good thing. I hoped I would get to live and make a difference to others. I should have been killed by that machine a million times bigger than me. But instead I ended up in the laps of my two very loving women and a big curious black thing called Dolly. Good things can come from terrible times. Remember that!

Monday was quite a day for me. I took a long nap. I had four legs when I went to sleep and three when I woke up. I was all wrapped in something green. I was pretty groggy and couldn't walk very well. I hurt, but then they gave me bad-tasting stuff and soon I didn't hurt as much. Everybody petted me a lot and said I was a fine little boy and had a winning personality, whatever that is.

Twenty-four hours later my new Moms from Julian came up in a shiny silver machine called a car and whisked me away from the hospital. All the trees whirred by and I got to rest on a very nice lap. I had no idea where we were going, but it was warm and it felt safe to be with my two new Moms. About an hour and a half later I arrived at a place they called home. I was hungry so I got some good food to eat and water to drink. It was swell. I have a really warm little cozy bed and all sorts of toys. I am not up to scampering quite yet.

I think I will like it here. I hope you like me. Keep your spirits up. After all there are many wounded souls like me who need love and kindness. I'll write again soon.

Until then….

Henry (aka Tripod, esq.), son of my Moms, brother to Dolly, friend to all.

I can't believe we have a cat.

You can't believe it!

Where on earth did he come from?

Henry:

I have a little tripod, too: her name is Tiger Lilly. She was four months old and her thoughtless owners left her outdoors with her brother and Mom for a long weekend, not understanding all the dangers in the big outdoors for one so small. Tiger somehow got her leg caught in a fence and was stuck for two or three days before I discovered her. I spent a week with her, trying valiantly to save that leg, but alas, it was just too much. The right rear leg had to come off. But within 24 hours she was hopping around in her cage at the vet like "Leg? What leg? Nothing wrong with me!" And she's been like that ever since. I've had her two months now and we're totally bonded. She is terrified of anyone else, and bolts for the closet at the least little sign of company coming. But for me she is just a little purr-box with tiger tabby stripes, black on grey, with white boots and chest and tummy. The neighbors who previously owned her were responsible enough to pay her medical bills, but decided they just couldn't keep her indoors, since they have three small kids who are in and out all the time. Just as well. Tiger Lilly is terrified of the kids. Life is good, and three-legged kitties do just fine.

– Love, BJ

Dear Henry,

We haven't met, but I feel as if I know you. My name is Tiger Lilly, but my Mom calls me Punkie (short for Pumpkin, she says). As she told you, I too am a tripod. You know, you and I are very special that way. We are one in a million…oh, well, two in a million. It's kind of cool to be part of such an elite group. I think we should form a tripod club; what do you think?

I am a couple of months older than you are. I lost my leg when I was your age, and today all my fur has grown back and the scar is all healed. Since it is my right hind leg I lost, I walk kind of funny – I sort of hop like a bunny, actually. My front feet work just fine, so I take a step and bring my hindquarters forward with a single hop. But I get around just fine. You should see me tear up and down the stairs.

You can reassure your Moms that you're not a bull in a china shop and you won't break anything…well, maybe just a couple things. We cats are really quite nimble on our three feet, and can do a delicate minuet over and around all kinds of artsy knick-knacks they have sitting around.

I'm fortunate that there are other cats here. Pookie has taken a liking to me (he's big, 14 pounds, pure alpha male) and he licks my head, grooming me. But I would rather play with him, so I bat at his whiskers — then he gets disgusted with me, and walks away. Pookie and Scooter both let me sleep with them on Mom's bed — we have a couple heating pads and we take turns sleeping on them. Personally, I prefer to crawl under the covers and sleep right next to Mom. She likes it too, as long as I don't start kneading her. She says my tiny claws are very sharp.

Max is the third male cat here and he is a total wus. I terrorize him every chance I get. He is bigger than I, but he's a fraidy cat. Mom yells at me to stop picking on Max — she picks him up and takes him under the covers to protect him from me. So sometimes we sleep with Max on Mom's right side and me on her left side. But when I get a chance, I crawl over her to pounce on Max. He is such a wimp.

There is a dog here, too. I was afraid of her at first, but she is very sweet and she doesn't bother me at all. I just have to be careful to stay away from her when she is eating. Mom says Fannie is very "food possessive"

— kinda weird. There seems to be plenty of food here, so I don't know what the dog is so worried about.

Anyway, it sounds like you are having a wonderful life in your new home. Just don't take any guff from that big black pony you live with. Fannie told me the black pony can be quite unfriendly sometimes — apparently she didn't like Fannie when she visited your house. Dogs! Who can understand them?

Just remind Dolly that you have claws. She will respect you, and you will rule the roost. I know lots of other cats who boss around big dogs — I think it's totally cool.

Bye for now,

— Tiger Lilly (aka Punkie)

Me-wow!

— Enter, Punkie

3—NEXT ADVENTURE

I'm Outta Here!
(Places to Explore)

Date: Thursday, November 11
From: Cathy
To: My Friends

This new world is sooooo interesting. For two days there were metal sticks all around me, not at all like the trees of my forest. They didn't smell right and I couldn't get my claws into them. I think I heard Mom call it a fence. Well, two days was enough of that. After all, I'm a guy who's used to roaming the whole world. Seven feet by seven feet isn't my cup of tea.

So, I climbed out. Wow, is this ever a BIG place! I went in the big room and Dolly went in my space (although I can't imagine why). When Mom came back in the bedroom there were feathers all around and stuffing from a toy of mine (looks like I escaped just in time!). Dolly then went out in the garage where they keep my food and water bowls. She found my breakfast before I did, jumped up on the counter, and ate ALL my food! Hmpf! So now my Moms are looking around for a higher place to put my food so I won't starve.

By the way, my Moms have names now. It only seems fair since they gave me mine. One I call Mom Cathy because that's her name. (I think it's a good sign that she has "cat" in her name, even though she swears that she's *not* a cat person.) She's very intrigued by everything I do, and guards me closely to keep me safe from the hungry black dog, Dolly. The other I call Dr. Mom because she's been caring for my wound. They tell me she is a retired physician. All I know is she's very gentle and smart.

Today, Mom Cathy came in with a big thing called a sheet. It has pretty sheep on it. When I look up I think I am back at pasture. The problem is, she pinned it so I can't climb out. It presents a challenge. But trust me, I have the will and I will find a way.

Dr. Mom decided to change my dressing. She took off my green garb and let my skin breathe. We were all surprised to see my stripes tattooed onto my skin. Dr. Mom said perhaps it was the C`reator's paint by number scheme. I am very glad. The lines on my body will help my hair remember where to grow back and make me the way I was before I took that nap.

This house has a lot of bright and shiny things that will be great fun to play with. There are windows that have many colors. It looks like a swell place for a guy like me. I am so glad to be out of the cold. I worry about my sisters. I hope they figure out a way to find a home. I think trading a leg for this was not a bad deal. One of my sisters is being adopted by my Moms' friend, so I will get to see her.

I keep my Moms very busy so they don't have any time to be upset about whatever they were upset about before I came into their life. I will do my best to make them laugh and challenge their minds. I am slowly making friends with the great big four-legged horse they call Dolly. She lies beside the metal thing and we look at each other.

I will keep you up to date on how I am training the trio in San Diego. They have a lot to learn about cats, but they seem to want to learn.

Warmly,

Henry, Esq. (aka Tripod)

From: Beth C.
To: Henry

I'm enjoying your story Tripod. And, yes, you are a very lucky boy to have found such a loving, special home. Try to behave if you can…and play with Dolly so that she will love you.

– Love, Beth

Century"…no point in letting them take you for granted. YOU could have gone anywhere; THEY are blessed you decided to grace THEIR abode!

Welcome to the family!!!

Your "aunt" in the jungle (where there are some REALLY big cats!),

– Nikker

P.S. I notice that you lost your left appendage. That's o.k. You can write me with your right one.

Date: Thursday, November 11
From: Puffer • To: T Henry

Dear T Henry,

I admired your story about being a cat in a dog house, but frankly, my dear, it sounds to me that once having gained your entry to the San Diego scene, you are FAR FAR better off to concentrate on being a cat. Cats have one credo: Dogs have masters, Cats have staff.

I think you HAVE caught on and are well on your way to training your staff. If you falter in your resolve (males sometimes DO) feel free toe-mail me at any time.

– Puffer

Subject: This is for the new kid on the block…
Date: Thursday, November 11
From: Nikker • To: Henry

Dear Henry, Henri, Tripod,

Right now, I give you an "A" for Adaptability. You're coming along, kiddo!

A suggestion: Instead of becoming a purr-fect "wuss" (I mean – the new mothers are super, the surroundings aren't exactly chopped liver, and the "black horse" doesn't know what's moved in on her yet)…but I suggest you play it cool and not stray too far from your cat-roots, i.e., remind everyone – preferably daily – that you are WONDERFUL, and they're LUCKY to have you! Under no circumstances acknowledge that you just won the "Kitty Lottery of the

Date: Thursday, November 11
From: Willie • To: Henry

Dear Henry,

You lucky guy! I'm sure your new Moms AND that big black furry animal will get used to you and your shenanigans very soon and you will all be one fur pile in the evenings on the bed. That's the big, soft thing that humans lie down on at night. Callie and I get to lie down on ours every day with our Mom. It's quite cozy.

I would have loved to see that big black dog eating your food up on that high thing. I used to be fenced in when we got fed but now Mom just puts our food in different places in the kitchen – but I have to eat fast or Callie will come over and finish mine up before I'm through.

– Love, Willie

Date: Thursday, November 11
From: BJG • To: Cathy C.

Henry looks great! Soft, longish fur.

I wonder which is easier to get along without…a back leg or a front leg?

Tiger Lilly gets around just fine, but her one big limitation is she can't jump from the floor to high places – not enough power in just one hind leg. She can jump from the floor to the bed, or to the sofa, but not from the floor to the kitchen counter, or to a desk. She needs something like a chair so she can make it in two jumps. But she can climb the cat condominium (which is 7 feet high, carpeted, with boxes and platforms) just fine. Goes all the way to the top and curls up in the crow's nest so she can be the mistress of all she surveys.

For physical therapy, I used a fishing pole with a string and a toy tied to the end – I call it "cat fishing." I had Tiger Lilly jumping and batting at it, falling down, getting up, learning how to re-balance her body with just the three legs. I got lots of laughs and she got lots of physical therapy.

Now she doesn't need the therapy anymore – we just do it for the laughs.

Our love to Henry….and Dolly

– XXX BJ

The ABCs of Trees

Date: Thursday, November 11
From: Auntie Mariam • To: Henri

Dear Henri,

I'm enjoying your photos. How interesting that your skin looks exactly like your fur. It looks like protective coloration, except that it doesn't protect you from cars. I'm sure Dolly is enjoying your toys and your food, but she will have to learn how to share.

The weather is getting cold here, which is more fun for Rajah and less fun for me. The pumpkins on people's steps have been gnawed by squirrels looking for seeds. Some of their smiles are lopsided. Soon they will be replaced by Christmas decorations.

—Love, Auntie Mariam

Date: Thursday, November 11
From: Henri • To: Auntie Mariam

Dear Auntie Mariam,

Mom Cathy takes lots of pictures of me. She has over a hundred in two days. I am not entirely sure what a picture is, but something flashes and then she goes into another room and emerges later with something that looks like me.

Everybody is impressed that my skin is so cleverly tattooed. Nobody seems to have known that about cats like me. I am not sure what a car is, and maybe if I am lucky I will never see one again, except from the inside.

Dolly wants everything that is mine. Since I have never had anything, that's OK with me. She seems to sort of like me. She is very big, but I just roll over on my back and she noses me to check me out.

The weather is getting very cold in the woods where I used to live. I hope my sisters are OK. One of them is going to come and live in a home next week. Maybe we can play. She is my favorite.

What is a pumpkin? What is a squirrel? And what is a Christmas decoration? All I know about is wind and rain, and trees and the leaves I used to chase and my sisters. Everything is so new. It is a bit much. I am going to go to take a nap now. It takes a lot of energy to train my new family about cats. I now live in a tent with sheep on the ceiling. And they think I am strange?

Love, your nephew,

– Henri

A squirrel is a large mouse with a huge, bushy tail. It loves to eat nuts and seeds, but in a pinch it will eat anything, even Christmas ornaments. I know this for a fact, because I once had a squirrel living in my attic. Christmas ornaments are bright, sparkly things made of wood, cloth, and glass. People bring a tree into the house and decorate it with ornaments and twinkling lights during the darkest and coldest days of the year. Perhaps it reminds them that light and warmth and growing things will return in the spring, which seems a long way off.

Perhaps after your Moms get used to you, they might consider adopting one of your sisters as a companion for you. After all, two cats are as easy to care for as one, and kitties don't need to be walked at 3 AM in the rain and snow when their tummies are upset.

    Love,

– Auntie Mariam

Date: November 11
From: Henri • To: Auntie Mariam

Dear Auntie Mariam:

    Wow, there sure are a lot of things I don't know about. Why would people take trees inside? All the ones that I climbed were outside. There were about a million of them where I lived. My favorite game when I lived outdoors was chasing leaves. There are millions of leaves at my old house. I don't see any leaves here, but then I don't see anything but my Moms and the black horse and some toys.

    I don't think my Moms are interested in another kitty. They are having a terrible time trying to remember I am a boy. They rub my tummy and tell me what a cute little girl I am. It will take awhile but soon they will understand. I am a macho boy and Dolly has no idea

---

Date: November 11
From: Auntie Mariam • To: Henri

Dear Henri,

A pumpkin is a vegetable that looks like a giant orange ball – one much too big and heavy to play with, except when it is a baby. One night a year people carve faces on them and put lights in them to make them look like scary people. They do it to scare away evil spirits, like mean dogs and cars with road rage. Before they put the light inside, they usually take out the seeds, which are very good to eat if you toast them with a little salt. Vegetables and seeds are food, though most kitty gourmands like you prefer tuna, chicken, and the occasional mouse tartare.

How did
we get
into this
situation?

Who's
"We"?

Get the
camera.

"This is a lot better than what I was reading."

what her life is about to be like once I get to feeling a little better.

Auntie Mariam, thanks for educating me. I don't want to appear dumb. Moms say we have enough of that in the world these days.

– Henri

Date: Friday November 12 • From: Auntie Mariam • To: Henri

Dear Henri,

People bring trees inside because they miss them. Everyone used to live outside, and some of our pre-human ancestors actually lived in trees. Now, oddly enough, humans kill trees and use the dead trees to build houses. In cold climates, they also burn trees to stay warm. Perhaps people should have stayed in warmer climes and left the trees alone. Of course, trees also die naturally, and eventually turn into peat, coal, and diamonds. But that's another story for another day.

Love, Auntie Mariam

"I'll tell you a secret: I have a lot to learn, so please be gentle with me."

"Don't worry: I WILL make it to the top.... Right after this nap."

CHAPTER 5

Ants, Uncles and Cousins

Subject: Greetings From Henry
Date: Saturday, November 13
From: Henry • To: Everybody

Dear Friends,

I really like my new home. It is warm and filled with good food and the black furry horse called Dolly lets me nuzzle with her sometimes.

I have lots of new "aunts" and a couple of "uncles." There were millions of ants in Julian but the kind I have here are different. They pick me up and cuddle me and tell me what a fine boy I am. The ones in Julian just crawled on me and made me itch.

I haven't been outdoors yet and I miss chasing leaves in the wind. I have something else that one of my Aunts gave me. It is a little ball with feathers. I chase it all the time. I love it. Dolly tore one of them up but I have three more. I told her she was a bad dog to do that to my toy.

I wonder how my sisters are doing. I heard Mom Cathy say that one of them was going to be adopted by my Aunts. I hope she comes and plays with me. I have been thinking about writing the other two before the Winter sets in. Maybe you could help me with my letter. I want them all to have a home. The only way I got mine was losing a leg and taking a very long nap. When I woke up my life wasn't the same. Do you think I should tell my siblings to bump into something and take a long nap? I don't really understand these things. I just wish they would all be out of the cold.

My Moms say I am good for them because they haven't thought about their problem (whatever that is) since I arrived. I think they are a bit nervous about life after I get my stitches out. There are so many fun, reflective things around here; I can hardly wait to bat them all with my paw.

Mom Cathy didn't like me kicking sand out of my litter box all over her bedroom. She got me a different kind. It is purple. (Everything in this house is purple.) I like it better. It is enclosed and I have privacy. I thought I was doing a good thing sharing my litter with my Moms. People are different from cats.

Aunt Elsie came to meet me yesterday. She always liked my Moms but felt they were a bit deficient because they didn't like cats. Now she thinks they are super. She brought me a really nice bear. I like it a lot.

My uncle Jim, in Julian, says I won the lottery of homes. He says it was well worth a paw. Uncle Jim looks like the kind of guy who would know.

Dr. Mom says that I am King Henry VIII, as I have already used up one of my nine lives. I think I will hang on to the other eight.

— Henry esq.

Date: Saturday, November 13
From: Willie • To: Henry

Dear Henry T. esq.: Whatta life you lead! And in such a lovely home. I, too, have a great home with two Moms…and another furry animal, whose name is Callie. Callie has been a real treat for me because my Moms don't play with me that much and Callie loves to play. At first she didn't, but now she seems happy to play with me except at 05:30. I seem to wake up at that time, when everyone else is sleeping. I try to wake up one or both of my Moms because I need to go out. I figure that from 10:00pm until 5:30am is enough time to sleep and then I must go outside to piddle. My Moms seem unhappy with this.

Yes, purple is a great color. Actually, I'm wearing a mauve collar right now, in the same color category. My Mom Beth says that it is the wrong color for a boy, but I really don't care.

— Love, Willie

Date: Saturday, November 13
From: Puffer • To: Henry

Dear T,

King Henry VIII had a number of "staff." (Some were treated more kindly than were others.) I am AMAZED that a horde of supposedly politically savvy women have succumbed to your charms, but so be it. Timing is everything and your timing seems to be propitious.

It is important to remember that Dolly can be a valuable ally. Don't EVER take the friendship of an ally lightly. Don't get TOO pushy and full of yourself and REMEMBER THIS, should you ever have daughters, THEY will be more important than you!

— Puffer

Thank Dog for my Cataleptic Interdimensional Loo. Now, if only it would dematerialize the deposits!

"Now, that has to lead somewhere."

Date: Saturday November 13
From: Henri • To: Auntie Mariam

Auntie Mariam:

Well, it is not exactly purple kitty litter: It is a purple box with a purple dome on it. I don't have a basement and I am not sure they want me to be in the carpeted bathroom. They think I will fall in the toilet, whatever that is. I do expect my sister to visit me. I found her a home after all. Well, maybe my Moms helped a little. I don't think my other two sisters are up for adoption yet. Mom worries about them. She says they will probably get killed in the woods in their first winter. That would make me meow a lot. Maybe they wouldn't have to give up their leg, but I hardly miss mine. I seem to be able to do everything just fine.

– Henri

Dear Henri

Purple kitty litter – how regal! Tell your Moms that even four-legged kitties rarely manage to keep ALL of the litter in the box—that's why their Moms tend to put litter boxes in the bathroom or basement. You may not have a basement, but perhaps your house is big enough for you to have your own bathroom! I hope your little sisters find homes before winter. I hope all the kitties in animal shelters find good homes, too – not to mention the puppies.

Once your sister goes to live with your aunts, don't be surprised if she doesn't especially want to visit you. Kitties tend to be homebodies, unlike dogs, who love to go exploring, both with and without their Moms and dads.

– Love, Auntie Mariam

Date: Saturday November 13
From: Auntie Mariam • To: Henri

Dear Henri:

It is unlikely your sisters would get killed in the woods (unless there are cars or snowmobiles). Kitties who live outside all the time are called feral cats, and they can live quite well on mice and birds, as well as on food that people sometimes leave out for them. Cats are excellent hunters. We knew some feral cats years ago in Vermont and we tried to tame them, but they preferred to live outdoors. Their only natural enemies were farmers with chickens.

I do not think you will fall in the toilet, but it would not be good for you to drink the water. Your Moms should remember to put the lid down. I once knew a kitty that would drink water only from the kitchen sink – preferably with the faucet running. Rajah loves the doggy drinking fountain in the park that burbles merrily, but it was just turned off for the winter. Some dogs stand on top of it in the summer, or lie in the cool mud at its base. Fortunately, the river cannot be turned off by the water department, so Rajah can still have a drink outside when he is thirsty. Rajah says moving water is tastier than still water. When I water the plants on the deck with the garden hose, he snaps at the water and gulps it down.

I am glad that you don't miss your leg. I hope the pain is gone.

– Love, Auntie Mariam

Date: Sunday November 14
From: Henri • To: Auntie Mariam

My Moms say that they can't put the seat down because they say it is a raised handicap seat, whatever that is. Seems a lot easier to use the woods or the box they got me.

My Moms can't even remember what pronoun to use with my name. I have been called "she," as in "Isn't she cute?", about a zillion times. I don't know why they can't remember. I try and give them my most masculine look so they will remember. They call Dolly "Dollygirl." So I guess I should be "Henryboy." Anyway, they are having a terrible time referring to Dolly and me by our appropriate gender. I guess I will have to be patient.

My leg that is missing only hurts some. Dr. Mom said one of my stitches is weeping so she has a watch on that. I feel pretty good. I am having fun but it is a big adjustment.

– Henri

This world is so amazing!

CHAPTER 6

Oh, Henry!

Date: Sunday November 14
From: Henry • To: All My Friends

Dear Friends,

Two-legged, supposedly normal, able-bodied humans are no match for me! One of my Moms spent a lot of time pinning my sheep sheet up like a tent. I lay in my second story bed and watched the whole thing, planning my exit. I guess humans don't think like a wily street-smart (except for once) kitty like myself. I could already see a spot I could fit my body through. I let her think she had made a kitty-safe enclosure so she would go back to her study and work. About a half hour later I made my exit and Dolly and I were playing happily in the kitchen. She came in and told me I was a bad kitty. Imagine that from a psychologist! I dusted off my self-esteem, gave her a look that told her I was smart, not bad. I let her spend a long time figuring out how I had gotten out. I'm going to let her think she fixed it, until I'm bored, and then out I go!

My Moms went to a party last night and left Dolly and me alone. Dolly comes and lies by my condo enclosure. Sometimes she cries. I only know kitty language so I have to learn why she is crying. I think she wants my food rather than my company, but I am not entirely sure.

I've had a lot of visitors. At first they say, oh poor little thing, he's so small. I don't exactly understand why they say that. Then I start playing with my feathers or running around the house and they say "he runs almost normal." They ask lots of questions, like

how big will I be? Who was my Mom? Where did I come from? How did I get hurt? Will I be normal? I don't know the answers to any of those things. I don't know why anyone cares. I was in the woods, and then I wasn't in the woods. I can run and play better than other kitties. I don't know what the word "normal" means but when they go out and leave the TV on for me, I hear a lot of things about what normal life is. Two-legged creatures seem quite obsessed with this word.

Life is more interesting for me since I became different from my four-legged sisters and you two-legged creatures. Used to be, I didn't have to think or be creative to get what I wanted. But my eyes and my purr saved me from a sleep that would have been permanent. I learned I could make people cry. I learned that I could help myself have a better life. Now I think it's payback time. It's my turn to teach them.

First of all, who cares where you came from? I don't need a pedigree to get into people's hearts and homes. Heck, here I am in San Diego with a three-story condo of my own. Not bad for a back woods kitty from Julian. My Mother had me and then she left me so that is enough about her. There are so many ways to move through the world. Who needs four paws? Three suits me just fine.

I don't know why people look at the space where the paw was. I do all sorts of clever things so they will notice what I *can* do, not what I *can't* do. I can do anything I want. I am unique in this world. My Moms love me. It is the time and energy and love they spend on me that makes me who I am. Nurture over nature. I have swell Moms! I know I make them nervous and I still have to train Dolly. But I've been here only five days. It took the Creator seven, if you believe such things, so I may have two more to go.

Mom Cathy has a friend that she says is not going to be joining the great flock of aunts I am collecting. She is Swiss-French and says she will become my tutor and I will be her pupil. And you two-legged things think *I'm* strange?

Last night the aunties that brought me my favorite toy, a ball with feathers, came over very late. A limo had taken them to this very special party and they made the driver stop and see me on their way home. They never had a limo ride before so they thought they would make the most of it. They oohhed and aahhed over me, kissed me on the nose, and put me back to bed.

Life is good. I don't think I want to be normal. I think life will work better for me just being Henry. I have my own secretary! Heck, it doesn't get much better than this! Dolly is trying to share center stage with me. Some days are better than others. I curl up next to her. Fur feels more familiar and comforting than skin.

— *Henry Esq.*

Date: Sunday, November 14
From: Auntie Mariam • To: Henri

Dear Henri,

What a lovely photo! You and Dolly look as cozy as any old interspecies couple, like Rajah and me. You and Dolly are lucky to have each other for company when your Moms go out. I'm glad you can escape from your enclosure. You must be feeling better, and nobody likes to view the world through the bars of a cage. I hope your stitches will come out soon, so you can have the run of the house.

This is what's known as a "doggly-woggly kittly-wittly snuggly-wuggly."

"How about some cat's-up on your cowlick?"

I must say that with your tutor and secretary, not to mention the aunties who make their driver stop the limo so they can give you a goodnight kiss, you sound a bit like the little girl named Eloise who lives at the Plaza Hotel in New York City. Do you call room service for fresh tuna and catnip?

It was a fine fall day today and Rajah and I had a nice walk. Tonight I am going to cook some chicken sausage with rice. If Rajah is a good boy I will let him lick the bowl.

— Love, Auntie Mariam

Date: Sunday, November 14
From: Henri • To: Auntie Mariam

Dear Auntie Mariam:

Dolly and I aren't actually allowed to "be" together when our Moms are out, just in the same room. I think that will change when we grow up. I played a lot in the house today. I think my sister is coming to visit me. I would cross my paws wishing it were true, but then I only have one front paw.

The girls who came by are recovering from a bad experience. Their house burned down in a bad fire and all their pets died. They almost died trying to save them. They lived with the women who had a 25th anniversary party and were given a gift of this ride. They had never been in a limo before so I thought it was neat they came to see me. What a good use of a driver.

My stitches need to be in for two weeks. One of them is draining, so Dr. Mom is keeping a watch on that one.

I don't know anyone named Eloise or what a hotel or New York City is. What is room service? Should I have it?

I miss the Fall, and chasing all the leaves. Life is filled with trade-offs. I like it here and my Moms are entertained by me. That is good. I hope they remember how much they like me when I start breaking things.

— Love, Henri

Dear Henry

My Mom found me in the woods of North Carolina, oh…years and years ago. I had all four legs, but was really starving. (I usually am, but back then, it was for real).

I heard a bunch of people saying that my Mom didn't want another cat, but the first time we met she picked me up, turned me on my back, I put my paws softly around her face, and she finally understood what I knew the minute I saw her. She knew that she must devote the rest of her life to making me totally happy. That meant new toys every year, a lot of attention, food on a daily schedule, and tidbits and treats.

In turn, I agreed not to "make mistakes" in the house. I don't have the same problem you do with litter boxes, as I would rather explode than use mine. So I wait until Mom leaves me out in the back yard.

Because I am a black cat, on Halloween Mom keeps me in for several days so neighborhood kids do not "get me" (whatever that means). Then and really, ONLY then, do I use that darn box.

Mom and I grew old together. She gives me thyroid medicine every day.

When she picks me up, I still wrap my paws softly around her face. It was love at first sight. And still is.

— Rhett Butler

Enter,
Mr. Rhett Butler

Dear Rhett,

I am glad to meet you. It is good to know someone else from the woods who is hungry. I did the same thing with my new Moms, only I turned on my back and just stared into their eyes until they decided not to put me to sleep. I already have been given a lot of toys from my new aunts and Dolly shares some of hers. Dolly isn't entirely sure she likes me. I would like to sleep with her because she is soft like my sisters. My Moms let us cuddle sometimes but then we go to our own beds.

What is a mistake? I don't know if I make them. I sort of like my purple litter box. I liked the woods better but I don't see any woods around. What is a back yard? I wonder if I have one, too? So many things to discover.

Why would the kids "get you" on Halloween?

What is Halloween?

Should I stop using the box and insist that I get to go to the back yard?

Mom Cathy says she has to take thyroid medicine every day. I don't know what that is. I take medicine now so my wound won't get infected.

I loved my Moms at first sight too. They would not have taken me if I hadn't had my accident. I guess accidents can be a good thing. Thanks for writing to me.

– Henry

Date: Sunday, November 14
From: Nicky • To: Henry

Hola, Henry!

Just wanted you to know I got your latest here in the jungle. Cute, cute picture of you and Dolly!

I'm going to introduce you to something new: it's called "The Law of Unintended Consequences" and it often works in strange ways. For example, your new Moms thought they were doing something altruistic when they took you in…but I think it's turning out that they are the ones receiving a gift…and don't you let them forget it! Remember: YOU had other options. It may not be true, but attitude can get you a long way in this world. Trust me!

In addition, you are sparing darling Dolly a possible neurosis from being an "only" child. I think it's just great that you are becoming friends, as your latest picture so well demonstrates.

One of the best things in having you around is that your presence seems to

"I just want Henry to feel normal."

have dispelled much angst in your household over recent losses. We won't go into details, but I have it on good authority that God was overheard saying maybe he shouldn't have rested on the seventh day. (Animals are purrrfect...people are not.)

The jungle is a long way away from anything you know about, but it is wonderful here, too. Just a few minutes ago I found a beautiful blue Morpho butterfly perched on the edge of my white couch in the living room. My doors are always open and I get many surprise guests, sometimes frogs, but most often birds. It's one of the little delights of living in Costa Rica. Let's make a deal: You keep me up to date on your adventures and I'll do the same with mine. OK?

Save a "cuddle" for me. . . . I'll get back up there one day.

— Nicky (your aunt in the jungle)

He's WHERE!?

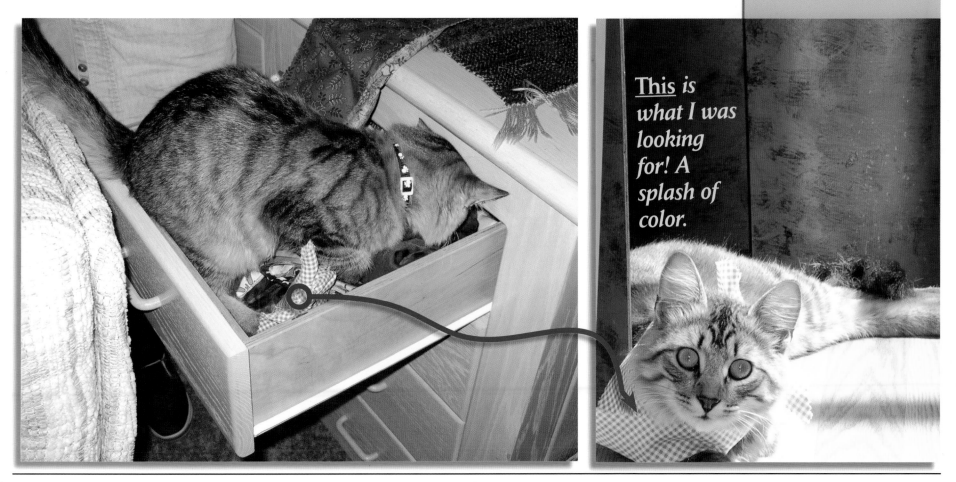

This *is what I was looking for! A splash of color.*

CHAPTER 7

Just Between Guys

Date: November 13
From: Henry • To: Uncle Bob

Dear Uncle Bob,

Thanks for noticing I am a smart boy. My Moms keep saying isn't she cute and say I am a good pupper. I think they suffer from gender confusion. Do you think I will grow up neurotic from these early episodes? From one guy to another, what do you think?

– Henry T

Date: November 13
From: Uncle Bob • To: Henry

Henry,

I guess you meant "puppy?" (Learning English IS tough.)

Anyway, in answer to your question: Your parents can be as confused as they like, and you can turn out neurotic or not. It doesn't matter. REMEMBER: YOU DON"T HAVE TO BE LIKE THEM!

Follow your passion! Join a group!! Write a Mission Statement!!! (That won't matter either.) You're a great and thoughtful cat and you've got great parents and also that big black thing to figure out and you live in a gorgeous house!

Just go on doing what you've been doing! Snuggle your Moms for me.

Uncle Bob from Oakland ("Oh my god, I'm corresponding with a cat!")

"I wonder what Henry's thinking?"

"Now, tell me: Do I look like a pupper to you?"

Date: November 13
From: Henry • To: Uncle Bob

When did I mean puppy? I can't be having a memory problem at four months old. (I did have a concussion.) Thanks for all your advice. They keep referring to me as "she." It is a little confusing. I got this very masculine name and then everybody says "she is so cute," etc. The big black thing is a challenge but I am working at it. Why is it so strange that you would be corresponding with a cat?

– Henry

Date: Sunday, November 13
From: Uncle Bob
To: Henry

Dear Nephew:

Re: "Puppy": "pupper" is a non-word. I thought this was a simple typo and you meant "puppy." Sorry if I misunderstood. Maybe there IS a "pupper?"

Ask Mom Cathy to explain the above to you.

Re: About those two-legged people. You're absolutely right. You're a smart kid (I mean cat).

— Uncle Bob from Oakland

Date: Sunday, November 14
From: Henry • To: Uncle Bob

Uncle Bob,
My Moms call puppies "puppers." They have a lot of initials after their names, but they also have a lot of special terms of endearment. Pupper is one of them. It is a word to them. What makes a word? If we understand it then is it a word? In this house "pupper" has common meaning. Now mind you, I am not one, but it seems to amuse them to refer to me as one. I just go with the flow.

— Henry, your nephew

CHAPTER 8

So Little Time (So Many Breakables)!

Date; Monday, November 15
From: Henry • To: All my friends

Well, today I was allowed in the living room. This is a very big house! The living room is about 1000 times bigger than my little space. Dr. Mom put me down to explore. Mom Cathy ran around with a silver thing in her hand that keeps going flash. Both of them kept saying, "Did you get that, that was cute!"

There are a lot of interesting things in this room. It is called a "living room." Up until today I lived in a room called a "bedroom." Because I **lived** there, why wasn't **it** called the living room? It seems to me that one lives in whatever room one is in. So tell me: Why aren't all the rooms called the "living room"? I wonder if one is supposed to do something different in this room from my other room? It's all very confusing.

I used to live under the sun and stars in the woods in the mountains. There were no fences, no enclosures, and no litter boxes, lots of leaves to chase and trees to climb. It was my living space. Why don't you people live outdoors? There is room for everybody and there are no rules or spray bottles or anybody saying "No." One just lives there. I guess the mountains in Julian were my living room. There was room to live and play and hunt and frolic. Don't get me wrong. I like it here. It is warm and the food is great. It just takes some getting used to. I like my Moms a lot and I think they like me.

As I explored many things in the "living room" Dr. Mom kept saying, "Well, that is the 'before' picture." Mom Cathy asked, "Before

what?" Dr. Mom said, "Before it all crashes down!" There are a lot of things here that they seem to think I could break. Why do people have so many things that they have to worry about guarding them or breaking them? Why isn't there just a room full of leaves that fly around and make pretty patterns? In my last home there were millions and millions of leaves. There were enough for everybody in the whole world to have some to play with. Leaves don't break. They are such fun to chase. Maybe all of you would like to empty your living rooms and put leaves in them. I will visit each one of you and show you what you do with them.

Today I also saw my first balloon. It was purple and very beautiful. I taught Dolly how to eat the ribbon. I batted the balloon with my one front paw. It was fun. Mom took another "before" picture. What do you suppose that means? Do balloons break?

Friends ask if I have been in the family room; another one of those confusing words. When I am in a room with my new family, does *that* become the family room? If my family and I go to the living room, is it then a family room because we as a family are in it? If we stay there a long time does it go back to being a living room because we are living there? I know I am just four months old, but you two-legged beings have certainly mixed things up with words and space. I've been told that this house doesn't have a family room. How can that be? We are a family and we have many rooms. Maybe somebody will explain it to me.

My Moms keep calling me "she." They named me Henry because it's a strong masculine name. They think cute means "she" and I am told that I am cute. I hope they get it together soon and remember I am a boy.

My Moms have initials after their names. I don't know what they mean, but I've been thinking of some after my name, so I can be like them. I tried Esq. but it didn't seem to suit me. I've thought about a lot of different initials, but none seem to fit. I keep thinking, I just

"Dolly, don't eat your kitty! Dolly, I mean it, bad dog, don't eat your kitty!"

"Henry, don't pop Dolly's balloon! Henry, I mean it, bad kitty, don't disappoint your doggy!"

"They seem to be completely smitten by this kitten. Even the black horse is as submissive as a canary."

want to be me. Then I thought, that's it! I will be Henry jm. Henry, **just me**! I sort of like it. What do you think?

Thanks for being my pals. So many of you are helping me understand my new world. Hugs and purrrrs to all of you.

– Henry jm

Date: Monday, November 15
From: Aunti Mariam • To: Henri

Dear Henri,

The first people's houses had only one room — usually a cave, which, naturally, was the living room — although nobody called it that. By the time people started calling a room the "living room" they were probably doing most of their living somewhere else — maybe in the kitchen or the "family room."

I think naming a room can be the kiss of death, don't you? If you go around naming your rooms, you feel guilty if you don't live up to

Date: Monday, November 15
From: Rhett Butler • To: Henry

Dear Henry,

You may not know this, but you are an "M" cat. Go to the mirror (and try not to break anything on the way) and you will see that you have an M in the middle of your forehead. Being an M cat means two things:

1. You are considered aristocratic in England;
2. M cats are usually the friendliest.

So if you want to call yourself Sir Henry, it is OK with me.

– *Your new friend, Mr. Rhett Butler*

the labels. For instance, what do you do with a "great room?" Stand around trying to act great? As a kitty, you understand that staking out your turf is more important than naming a room. Whose room is it, anyhow? If another cat comes into your room, you might just pee all over the rug to impress upon her that it's your room. That's what counts, right? Whose pee you smell when you come into a room?!

– *Love, Auntie Mariam*

Dear Mr. Rhett Butler:

I went to the mirror and I *do* have an "M" over my eyes. What an observant guy you are. (By the way, I didn't break anything on the way there, which is a wonder because there are mirrors all over this house.) I keep thinking I have a playmate, I run up to it and bang; it is just a cold piece of something flat. I keep checking for that kitty who looks an awful lot like me inside that flat hard piece of whatever it is. So far, no luck, but I will keep trying.

I overheard Mom Cathy having a conversation yesterday. She said all her life she grew up hating cats. She is a dog person. She said she never had a cat and just knew she wouldn't like one. I guess her mother loved birds and therefore hated cats so Mom Cathy grew up also hating cats. I don't know yet what a bird is, but if someone likes it I guess they don't like me. That makes me a bit predisposed to not like birds. I will keep an open mind because I really don't know what one is. Maybe Mom Cathy's Mom was wrong. By the way, Mom Cathy hates lima beans too, but admits she has never tasted them.

I don't understand how you know you hate something you have never known or tried. What kind of sense does that make? I am only four months old and have much to learn, but already I know some things I like better than others. I like the food that is pink more than the food that is brown. I know that because I tasted it. (Mind you, I am quite willing to eat the brown food if there is no pink; both are better than what I used to eat.) I know I like to curl up close to fur better than skin. It feels more familiar and warm so I love to cuddle with the black horse called Dolly. I had never been held the way my Moms hold me, but I like that a lot too.

It seems in the world of two-legged creatures, words are a common source of misunderstanding. I don't know who made them up. I think people would be better off and get their needs met more if they

Mmmm

"Talent, beauty, two Moms, e-mail – plus the fact that I'm an 'M' cat! What more could I ask for?"

PUNKIE

"A tripod am I – and proud of it!"

looked deeply into each other's eyes, purred a lot and swished their tails. I wonder how I could get them to understand?

I think sometimes people hate what they don't understand. Mom Cathy looks at me every day and wonders why she thought she hated animals like me. She says I am a good teacher. I am not sure what that means but as long as it means I get to stay around, that's fine with me.

– Love, Henry

Date: November 15
To: Henry • From: Punkie

Dear Henry:

You are an only cat. Your Moms are dog people. You are going to be the one and only. I love your saying that you got in by accident (tee hee). You're a funny guy! I like that in a cat!

My Mom was always only a cat person – the dog is a new thing for her. But now she loves dogs too – so I guess she has switched from AC to DC (from All Cats to Dogs and Cats). I don't really know if she likes all dogs but she loves the one we have. I know Scooter is her favorite cat because I overheard her on the phone one day (she didn't know I was listening)…but I am being really adorable, and I think I might become her favorite soon. I have the advantage because the other cats go outdoors all day long and I get to have Mom all to myself (except when Scooter sleeps in - but sooner or later he goes out too). I purr real loud when she talks to me, or when she pets me, and she likes that. I hang out wherever she is in the house – I'm like the company. So maybe I'll be the top cat one day soon.

OK, it's late now, and we all gotta go pick out our spots on the bed to settle down. G'night, Henry. hugs,

– Punkie

Date: Tuesday, November 16
From: Henry • To: Punkie

Dear Punkie,

Thanks for writing to me. Mom says I have over a hundred e-mails to me in a week. I don't know what an e-mail is, but the way she said it made me feel special. I have so many aunts and uncles and one tutor. I thought I was unique in all the world because I was a tripod. I am glad there are others like me. My Mom told me that there was a book she loved that talked about what made one special. I think she said it is called *The Little Prince*. (I like the title because I consider myself a little prince.) It said something like "it is all the time that is spent on you that makes one unique in all the world." At first look, each of us might look the same, but we are unique because of how we are loved and cared for. I think it is cool to be only one of a few in the world. Imagine our finding each other. I bet Mom could find a bunch of others on her computer. I like the computer because I can sit on the keyboard and push down on the keys.

You are a clever girl, AC/DC. I like that! I may use it when I write to my friends. I will tell them you thought of it. I think I will always be top cat and bottom cat because I am an OC (only cat). Hey, I am collecting initials. I have a friend, Puffer, who says I should put initials in front of my name, and have it be just one — I Henry. I am practicing with it. I am not sure. Let's see, I Henry, jm oc. I could get people wondering with all those letters.

I am glad your fur grew back. I was a little worried. If yours did, mine probably will too.

My Mom says your Mom is looking for the right man. Why? It sounds as if you have a house of perfect pets?

I will tell my Moms to cool it with the breakage deal. I haven't broken anything yet, except my leg.

I don't have any other cats here, just the black horse called Dolly.

"There's lots of this stuff outside. Why don't they just let us eat out?"

"Now, what was I just thinking?"

"I wonder why they say that grass is bad for you?"

She is nice to me most of the time but sometimes pounces. I think she wants to play, but she is so big. I get under the covers. It is very nice there. My sister got adopted by a friend of my Moms. I can't wait to see her again. A cat in LA named Rhett Butler is writing to me. He is very clever. I think I will like him. I have had offers for dates from mature female cats. I am not sure what a date is, but they are really pretty cats.

Bye for now. And thanks for being my girl friend. I like you.

Your friend,

– Henry jm

CHAPTER 9

Messages for Henry

"Don't tell me I'm not supposed to be here, because this is where I am."

Enter, Emmy Lu

Date: Wednesday, November 17
To: All my friends • From: Henry

Wow! I am making so many new friends. I have cats writing to me from around the world! One of them, an older girl, but very pretty, wants to know if I want to date. I must admit I don't know what that means, but I wrote back and said she was very pretty and I thought I would like to do whatever she suggested. I haven't heard back from her, but I have her picture posted on my compound.

I've made two new friends in L.A. One is a tripod like me, only she is minus her back leg. She wants us to make a club of tripods. I don't know what a club is, but Tiger Lilly (Punkie for short) writes such nice things that I would do whatever she wants to do. My Mom met her Mom and liked her, so we would probably like each other. Punkie is teaching me how to train my Moms and Dolly. She is six months old and very worldly. She knows way more than I do because of her amputation. She lost her hair just like me but because she had stripes on her skin it remembered where to come back. That was very reassuring to me.

Your friend, Henry jm

Date: Wednesday, November 17
To: Henry • From: Emmy Lu

Dear Henry,

You are a precious, precious boy. I love hearing about all your adventures and especially your philosophy on life. You are very worldly for only being four months old. Thank you for all the wonderful pictures and stories. I really look forward to getting them. In fact, I've started a whole folder on my e-mail just for you. You are very lucky to have such wonderful Moms. If you listen to them you will grow up happy and healthy. Be a good boy and grow big and strong. Every day is a new adventure – enjoy each and every one. Rest up!*

Much love from us all,

– Emmy Lu, Weeds, Newby, Sissy and Dee – your paw-pal cats in Bremerton (except for Dee – she's the Mom)

Date: Thursday, November 18
To: Emmy Lu • From: Henry

Hi Emmy Lu, and all your sibs! I wonder where Bremerton is? I also wonder what a folder is? It sounds like a good thing to have. Are there leaves to chase in Bremerton?

I like my Moms. They don't know anything about cats. I have a lot to teach them. Some cats from other places are writing me on how to train them. It is very helpful. They are learning a bit more day by day.

I was sleeping and now I want to play. Mom says it's too early. How could it ever be too *anything* to *play*? Humans are funny that way. Thanks for writing.

— *Henry, jm*

Date: Wednesday, November 17
To: Henry • From: Puffer

I've been calling you "T," but if you think you want initials after your name, I'd rethink that if I were you. How about putting initials before

"Boy, there is so much to do around here!"

your name instead? How about "I" (as in aye). Who is in charge? You are, and don't let anyone assume you are not!

Serve notice on everyone. I, Henry, (think Descartes… you "AM" because you say you "AM"…)

AYE, AYE, Henry (ask your Auntie Sue about that if you don't understand Navy talk and she'll explain it).

I'm going outside now and chase lizards in the rosemary hedge and wait for some dumb old birds to come and eat the pyracantha berries just in back of the rosemary hedge. For dessert I'll find a mouse that thinks it's hidden. HAH! Yummy buffet. I hope you can make it outside soon yourself.

You have all the women where you want them but I'd keep an eye on Dolly. (Dawgs do have their Moments of revenge.) My favorite place to sleep inside the house is on the bookshelves. Mom has floor-to-ceiling bookshelves with lofted ceilings, and some are twelve feet tall. Great place to hide and be overlooked when Mom is calling me and I do NOT choose to respond! One of my favorite spots on a book shelf is curled over and around Shakespeare. I have learned some dandy

"Why do I always dream of paws?"

"What if Dolly were this small?"

insults there, and here is one for you to say to Dolly if she tries to horn in on your act: *"Thou gorbellied milk-livered wagtail!"*

Deliver that line and then do a fast exit off stage.

— *Your country cousin, Puffer*

Date: Wednesday, November 17
To: Puffer • From: Henry

Dear Puffer,

You seem to be a really wise cat. You must be way older than I am. I keep trying out different names, T, Henry jm, I sort of like I Henry also. Thanks for your suggestions.

Dolly is a pain sometimes but I am too little to do anything but roll over. She doesn't know that I am going to grow. Will she ever be surprised!

I miss being outdoors. That is the only world I know. It is nice and warm in here. I have toys but they are not as much fun as chas-

ing leaves. I think I am going back to Julian on Saturday. Maybe I will see two of my sisters. Everything is so different now. What a world. Thanks for being my wise friend. Catch a lizard or mouse for me. Someday I will get to go out in the yard.

— *I, Henry jm*

Date: Thursday, November 18
To: Henry • From: Puffer

Dear I,

Almost everyone IS older than you are, silly kitten! I am young and beautiful!! Mom had a well loved cat named Monica Mellow WMBC who lived to be 23. (The WMBC stood for "World's Most Beautiful Cat.") She has her own place and plaque in the garden now where she liked to do the backstroke through the chives. Everything I know, I learned from Monica. SHE was the wise one. Since you DON'T have a Monica to help you, I'll give you suggestions from time to time. But you DO seem to be off to a good start.

Monica liked to ride in the car with Mom and even walked with her on a leash when they went to strange unsafe places. I do NOT like to go in the car, nor do I like leashes. Monica was far more adventure-some than am I. It worked for her. I have my own agenda. You will find what works best for you. Every cat gets to decide. Even YOU!

You looked tired in your last picture. Be sure you learn to relax so you'll have time to dream up new things for your Moms And Many Aunts (MAMAs) to do for you.

— *Puffer, your country cousin*

Date: Thursday, November 18
To: Puffer • From: Henry

I must be older than some kitties. I have aged since my accident. I try and frolic in cute ways to seduce my dog-loving Moms into liking me more and being glad that they saved my life.

I am going to have to learn about life from Dolly the dog and my Moms. There are no other cats here and I am quite sure there won't be another one. I got here by accident.

What is a leash? Should I get one? Mom goes on walks with Dolly. Maybe she would take me if I had a leash. Where do I get one?

I have only been in a car twice. I liked it. All the trees whirred around me. I have also only had one bath. I liked that too.

I am not sure what I am going to decide. I was tired but I am feeling more perky now. Good night.

— I, Henry jm

Date: Thursday, November 18
To: Henry • From: Puffer

Dear I,

I don't believe anything REALLY happens by accident to cats. I didn't get here by accident. You didn't get there by accident. Look how well it worked out for both of us!

You might like a leash. Cat leashes are made of very light nylon cord and are attached to very lightweight nylon harnesses. Pet stores have them. Your MAMAs will know where to look for cat harnesses and leashes.

They are VERY resourceful women and will know just where to go to find them. A leash and harness (they would trust) might even get you outside sooner to find some leaves. This time of year is a GREAT leaf finding time.

Monica Mellow was great on a leash. She would go anywhere gladly except over sand at the beach, where she sort of floated. People who saw her being walked were always amazed. Watch and see how proud Dolly is to be walked. You can do it. You can do anything you choose to do. Who knows, maybe you could persuade Dolly to take you for walks! That would draw a crowd! Rest up now and dream good dreams.

— Your country cousin, Puffer

Date: Thursday, November 18
To: Puffer • From: Henry

It HAS been a hard day, typing letters, exploring my new house. I think my paws are a little swollen. Dr. Mom says I should elevate them above my heart. She's boss. Up they go. Good night.

— Henry jm

"I guess 'elevation' is not a form of play."

CHAPTER 10

Lessons and Llamas

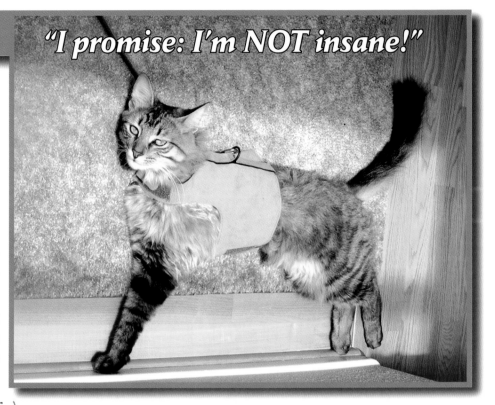

"I promise: I'm NOT insane!"

Date: Friday, November 19
From: Henry • To: Puffer

Dear Puffer,

I will see if I can get them to go and get me a leash and a harness today. Right now a harness might hurt my stitches, which will probably come out on Saturday. I don't hurt as much any more.

Well, I did have an accident and then I got here so I figured I got here via accident. Maybe not. I don't know what sand is. Is it like the stuff in my litter box? There are so many things to learn. I am a lucky boy to be having so many cat teachers like you. Thanks.

— *I Henry jm (I am still deciding just what part of my name I will keep)*

Date: Friday, November 19
From: Puffer • To: Henry

Dear I,

You ARE an early riser ! Good for you !

Your MAMAS will see that not all harnesses are designed the same. There WILL be one out there with your particulars in mind. If not, I am confidant that among those MAMAS is a clever lady who could design one for you. (I'll bet they are cognizant of the current provisions of the Disabilities Act and would jump at the chance to engineer one just for you).

— *Your country cousin, Puffer*

Date: Friday, November 19
From: Henry • To: Puffer

Dear Puffer,

Tee hee! I like the picture of my Moms jumping at anything, even if it is a chance. Right now I have a collar with a little bell. Is that OK for a leash to go out with? It is a little big for me but I like it OK.

Am I covered by the provisions of the Disabilities Act? (whatever that is) Do I have a disability? I don't feel as if I do.

My Mom and I look for worms in the morning. Since we are early birds we should find a few. Dolly goes somewhere early in the morning, I cuddle with Dr. Mom, and then they come back in over an hour. Dolly jumps up and down when she knows she is going where ever they go.

— *I Henry*

Dear I,

My Mom and I start the day very early reading overseas newspapers. Then the east coast papers and hit the west coast about six a.m. I sit on her lap and wave my tail over the keyboard. She has explained to me that isn't especially good for the keyboard, but I DO like to keep informed.

It seems to me that you have good instincts about how to survive and who is most apt to assist you in doing just that. THAT is a short version of what the Disabilities Act is all about. You understand just fine for a callow youth! Don't play dumb with me, young man!

The bell and collar are cute but not practical when attached to a leash. My Mom has a dog named Pokey. They go places together. Pokey showed up one day claiming to be a lost, deserted, abandoned, woebegone puppy in need of a home, love and care. Accidental? HAH! Mom's son found her on the side of the road miles from everywhere and brought her here. You have Dolly and I have Pokey. They have their place I suppose but they are no match for us.

Just be glad your Moms don't have a llama. My Mom has one. No one messes with Uncle Louie. He is one impressive llama. I can kid myself that I am in charge here. Uncle Louie and I both know that HE is in charge. So, carry on.....but keep an eye out for llamas.

— *Your country cousin, Puffer*

Dear Puffer,

Thanks for the warning. My Moms have a friend who puts llama poop out in the garden to grow things. He wants to know if my Moms want some of it for their place in Julian. I thought it was a benign offer. Maybe it is like the camel getting his nose in the tent: first comes the poop next the llama??

Why does anybody have one of those animals, and why does your Mom want an Uncle Louie? Maybe if you teamed up with all the other animals Uncle Louie would be toast. Mom reads the news too. Not so much nowadays. It is too depressing. It is more fun to play with me. I like the keyboard too.

Why can't a leash be attached to my collar? Dolly gets one on hers. What's good for the goose is good for the gander, as they say on the farm. Have a good day.

— *I Henry*

Dear I,

Llama poop is magical! Use it by all means! Uncle Louie will never be toast and we'd be really dumb to even try that. He is a gift from the goddess and we appreciate him.

You said your collar was loose. It will slip right off your nose (which would be a good thing if you were an outside cat and it got hooked on something) but cat leashes need to be attached to harnesses. Harnesses are not to be worn all the time, just when you want to go outside and a leash is to be attached. Your Moms would be left standing there with a collar and leash and you'd be headed for the nearest pile of leaves.

Dolly needs a collar for her leash in order to take proper walks. Pokey needs a collar for the same reason. They are dogs. You are not. What's good for the dog is not necessarily good for the cat (or goose or gander)

It is time for my morning nap.

— *Your country cousin, Puffer*

CHAPTER 11

I'm Off!

Date: Friday, November 19
To: Henry • From: Punkie

*T*hanks for writing about me in your letter. You and I actually look a lot alike — grey with black stripes—except your fur is longer and mine is shorter. They call me a grey tabby. Since your hair is longer, I don't know if you are a tabby, too. Do you have white boots like I do?

I actually had two surgeries — about a month after I lost my leg, my Mom took me back to the vet and this time I had an operation on my tummy. Mom called it "getting spayed." She explained that they fixed me inside so I won't have any kittens. There are too many kittens in the world, my Mom says, and not enough homes for them. I don't know where kittens come from, but I guess it doesn't matter now, because I won't be having any. It's OK with me cuz there are six cats in this house already, and it would get crowded with any more.

Missy and Sandy aren't allowed to come in the house because they pee on things, Mom says. But they have a very nice yard to live in, with patio furniture to lounge on, several cat beds (covered in plastic so they stay nice and dry and warm when it rains), and a huge cat condominium covered with carpeting — it's HUGE. The whole yard is like a big cat haven, so Missy and Sandy have a nice life outside. Only the boy cats are allowed to come in at night and sleep, since they don't pee on things. I am the only girl cat allowed inside, cuz I don't pee on things either. I don't see why those other girls want to pee on Mom's pretty things in the house. It's very unladylike.

Scooter is kinda lazy, so he sometimes stays in the house with me during the daytime. He sleeps on the heating pad on the chair. Nobody but him ever sleeps there. I notice that the cats here, and the dog too, all kind of have their favorite places staked out. Pookie was sniffing around the dog kennel next to Mom's bed this morning, and Fannie the dog lunged at him and pushed him away. She never bites any of us cats, but sometimes it looks like she might. She is very possessive of her food and gets very angry if any of us cats come too close while she's eating. I feel kinda sorry for her, outnumbered by all of us cats.

Sometimes I get out in the yard for an hour or so, but I am afraid and I stay very close to the house. I sort of scoot around in the bushes. I know I can't run as fast as the other cats, so I stay very close to the house — I can run in the door if I get too scared. The world outside seems big and scary to me — kids walking to school making lots of noise, big cars go by sometimes, and I hear that there are coyotes out beyond the fence. I am so glad that Mom had that fence built to protect all of us cats. The yard is our own personal cat haven — it's very nice. And we share it with Fannie, who barks when people come to the gate with packages.

Mom is going to feed me now, so I have to go. Glad you are having such great adventures in your new home. And you have an ocean view too! Wow, think of all the fish in that ocean. I like to eat fish a lot, do you? Tuna is the only kind I've had so far, but it is yummy.

Bye for now,

— Your tripod girl friend, Punkie

Date: Friday, November 19
To: Henry • From: Puffer

As I was dropping off to snooze, I realized I hadn't told you Uncle Louie's real name. It is Odegos, which is, I think, old Greek for "guardian and protector." We call him Uncle Louie because he is a beautiful tri-colored llama and he reminds us of the handsome and wonderfully kind and generous Greek uncle of a good friend in San Diego.

That's your trivia for the day!

And now to snooze.

— Puffer

"I'm the shy, retiring type, unlike Henry, who can just be soooo in-your-face."
— Iris

Date: Friday, November 19
To: All my friends
From: Henry

Yea! I am going back to my mountain home in Julian. I will get to see my two sisters and play. I am so excited! I think I will go to the vet and also get my stitches out.
Talk to you all later.

— Henry jm

Date; Friday, November 19
To: Henry • From: Punkie

You are so lucky, Henry! My brother and mother live next door but I never get to see them. Oh well, I did go visit about a month ago and stayed overnight, but the small humans in that house scared me to death. I spent the night hiding under the bed. Those tiny humans make sudden moves and lots of

"I'm an avid newspaper reader, unlike Henry, who seems to read only e-mail, whatever that is! It might even be just a rumor!"
— Kira

But it's OK: my human Mom is the best. She lets me sleep with her at night, and sometimes we take a nap on the sofa, too. When she is working at her computer, I sleep behind her butt on her big chair, since she perches on the edge of the chair there is plenty of room for me. She is the one who rescued me from the fence where my leg got mangled, took me to the hospital, and nursed me through days and weeks that followed — so as far as I am concerned, she is my real Mom. She doesn't have fur, but her body is nice and warm all the time, so I snuggle up to her whenever she's not walking around.

Have a good weekend, Henry! Good luck with your stitches!

— Purrrrr, Punkie

"I like the sun. Henry does, too, but he doesn't sit still! I like to hang out and work on my tan."
— Gigi

noise, which bothers me. Mom says I am high-strung. I am like my cat mother — who is also scared of the tiny humans. She rarely goes in their house — she hangs out in the yard instead. Only my brother, Blackie, is not afraid of the tiny humans. They pick him up and play with him — but I am still afraid.

CHAPTER 12

I'm Back!

Date: Friday, November 19
To: All my friends • From: Henry

Hi everybody. I am home. It was quite a trip. Mom says I wasn't quite as good a rider on the trip up as I have been before. I was wiggly. I was really excited to be going back to my first home and to see my sisters. I could hardly wait. My Moms said we had to go to the vet to get my stitches out. I was nervous as we got to the vet. The last time I was there I took a long nap and woke up and was missing something. They were all glad to see me at the vet and told me what a good boy I was. I tried to be brave as he pulled on my wound. I cried only a little. Whew, he got *all* those stitches. Then, off we went to see my sisters. *meooooow* **:-)**

The car window was open and I could smell all the familiar smells I grew up with. I trembled with excitement as we drove into my driveway. There was a wonderful wind and my beloved leaves were flying around in the air. I wanted to chase them, but my Moms said not yet. Mom Cathy went and got my sisters while Dolly and I waited in my house. Only two came. I was told that Aunt Eugenie and Aunt Joanne adopted my other sister. I went bounding up to Gigi and Kira, ever so glad to see them. They sniffed me all over and then walked away. I thought my heart would break. I went up to them again and they just sort of stood there. I meowed and told them, "Hey, it's me, remember me, I have just been gone for a little while." They listened politely but wouldn't play with me even though I brought out my treasured feather toy to share with them. My Moms went and got some really good food so we could all crowd around the dish and eat together. Well, that worked. They were very excited to eat with me, but when we were through they went to the other part of the room. My Moms tried a few other things so that they would play with me, but they weren't the same as when I left them, or they thought *I* wasn't the same. I don't know if it was because I lost a part of me and walked funny, or that I smell like San Diego instead of Julian, or that they have short memories. It made me cry *meeooooowL* **:-(**

After a bit, my Mom put them outside and Dolly and I stayed behind. I think Dolly felt bad for me. She went and got a ball and started to play with me. I wasn't much in the mood because my feelings were hurt. She took her paw and nudged me to try and get me out of my funk. The problem was that she nudged me on my scar and it split apart a little. She didn't mean it; she was just trying to cheer

me up. Dr. Mom took me into the bathroom and tried to bandage the place that had opened. It didn't really hurt, but my Moms were worried. I played some, ate some, and explored my second home. It is a swell place, just like my other home.

The next morning Dr. Mom didn't like how my oweee looked, so off to the vet we went. I was nervous again. They looked at me and put some glue on and glued the spot that separated back together. They all *goooed* over me again, so I felt better.

I tried again with my sisters, but again they were not very interested in me. I still love them; I wonder why they don't love me any more. It is sad and confusing. I went in the bedroom to be by myself. It was there that I met "the three bears." I was feeling bad, so I cuddled up in their arms. They whispered in my ear that they would love me and

they would welcome me back always. For the rest of the weekend when I was feeling bad I went back on the bed to the welcoming arms of the bears.

I got to meet my Uncle Mike from Virginia. He stayed over Saturday night at my house. He said I was a wonderful kitty. He knows because he and his friend, Kevin, are "cat people."

In the middle of the night we all woke up to a lot of noise. My Moms said it was thunder, they said it was *raining* very hard. They said it was *hailing*. I am not sure what either of those words mean, but they seemed excited. After the sun came up, everybody was excited. They all said, "It's snowing, it's snowing!" White stuff was falling from the sky. Lots of it. I watched it as it fell. It is very pretty. Dolly went out in it. She ate it, pawed it and frolicked in it. When she came in she had white all over her black. I wanted to go out, but my Moms said *not yet.*

We stayed for a couple of hours watching the snow. It was fun. My sisters were put in the barn so they didn't get wet. I guess that is where they will live at night now. I am glad that they will be warm and well-fed, even if they don't remember I am their only brother.

I am glad I went to Julian. I am sad about my sisters but I have so many good things in my life that it is OK. I have lots of new friends and playmates and Dolly is learning to be a little gentler with me. It will take time but I will win my way into her heart just as I am into my dog-people Moms' hearts. Soon I will play with my leaves again, feel the wind in my face, and jump up and down in that white stuff named snow.

Thanks for caring about me.

– Love, Henry jm

Date: November 22
To: Henry • From: Punkie

Dear Henry:

Oh, growing up is so hard, isn't it? Most of us cats have to grow up and leave our families to make our own way in the world…but it is hard when it happens so soon. I had a similar experience with my cat Mom a couple weeks after I lost my leg. She came over to my house to spend the night before she went to the Vet to get spayed (she got spayed a few weeks before I got spayed. I guess it's something they do to girl cats). My Mom put me in the laundry room with my cat-Mom so I could keep her company overnight (the laundry room is sometimes a cat infirmary, and it was my home for the first few weeks while I was recuperating from my trauma). Well, my cat-Mom didn't want my company at all. She hissed and didn't seem to recognize me at all. I must admit, I wasn't sure I recognized her, either. I guess Mother Nature made us that way…so that we don't cling to one another, but rather we go out into the big world and our own lives. I think we're different from humans that way — they seem to remember each other for years, maybe forever, and like to get together with their Moms and sisters again. Maybe dogs are that way too — maybe they have a better memory for their families. But we cats forget very quickly.

I don't think about my cat-Mom or my brother at all anymore. I am totally bonded to my human Mom and she's the one I love. She kisses

me, cuddles me under the covers at night, feeds me, and lets me walk all over her when she's lying on the couch reading the paper or something. Whenever I hear her voice, I start purring. She makes me feel safe and loved.

I know you have two wonderful Moms who love you very much and your sisters have their own Mom to love them. Don't worry, Henry, you'll soon forget your sisters ever existed and you'll be very happy. Life has its disappointments, but

fortunately we cats live in the now and don't dwell on the past. Be here, be now, be happy. Life is good. And you're a lucky cat. I think that's what they should have named both of us tripods — Lucky. We are Lucky Stripes! hee hee

    – Hugs, Punkie (aka Tiger Lilly)

Date: Tues., Nov. 22
To: Punkie
From: Henry

Dear Punkie,
There have been a few bumps in my road to growing up, but generally I am having a really nice life. Several really smart cats write to me so I learn good stuff. You, Rhett Butler and Puffer are my favorite. You are a great tutor. I have a Henry file for all my letters. I now have 200 in it. They make my Mom laugh. I like it when she laughs.

Maybe Mother Nature is really smart. I want to make my own world and my world is way different from theirs. Why do humans want to get together with their old families? Does that make them clingy?

All I really think about now is toys, food, sunny spots to sleep, my Moms, and all my new friends. I feel safe and loved here. I like the name Lucky, but I like Lucky Stripes even better. You're so clever.

    – Purrs…. Henry jm

CHAPTER 13

Traveling Tips

Date: Tuesday, November 23
To: Henry I • From: Puffer

Dear I,

*T*ell *your Moms to put a towel over your cat carrier but arrange it so you can see at least one of them. Something you REALLY like should be inside the carrier with you. You'll like being in car a whole lot better that way. I don't go much in the car but Monica Mellow did. She went in the car enough so that eventually she didn't need the carrier. Mom used to take her somewhere every day in the car just so she'd get used to it. I never liked the car or traveling. Mom respects that and I don't HAVE to go in the car very often. She says "it's for your own good." HAH ! Her idea of "good" and mine are two different things. Monica Mellow got to do pretty much what she wanted and so do I. I CHOOSE not to go and complain about it bitterly when it's one of those "it's for your own good" times.*

You have many new memories that your sisters do not have and they continued with their lives while you were out gathering your new memories. Don't be sad for them. Everyone owns their own memories. Think of what wonderful new memories you have.

Thank you for the pictures. Some day maybe I'll send you pictures of me and Pokey and Uncle Louie. Your MAMA Sue had pictures of Pokey and Uncle Louie at one time, but I don't think she ever had a picture of me. What a shame ! I am by FAR the best looking.

— Puffer, your country cousin

Date: Tuesday, November 23
To: Puffer • From: Henry

Dear Puffer,

My Mom's put a blanket over my carrier. It still made me cry. I didn't have anything in there I really, really liked. Everything I really like was sitting in the front seat. Mom took me out of the carrier and I spent the rest of the trip in her lap. I shook a little, but then the sun shone on me, so I napped a bit.

You are really right about memories. I will remember that. Every day, I have a great time and then tomorrow it becomes a great memory. Mine will be different from theirs. Animals (and people, I suppose) either grow together or they grow apart. I am growing together with Dolly and my Moms and all my new aunts, and growing apart from my sisters. It was just a surprise at first. You and some other really smart kitties that write to me all told me the same thing, so it must be true. Don't you have any pictures of yourself to send me? I love knowing what somebody looks like.

Are you better looking than I am?

— Love I (Henry jm)

Date: Tuesday November 23
To: Henry • From: Puffer

Dear I,

Monica Mellow had a plaid Pendleton "throw" that was **HERS.** *Wherever she was, she had her "throw." It defined home base for her in the car, camper, on a brief outing, or on a long trip across country. Monica would ride on the seat next to Mom and go to sleep if the "throw" was put on the seat. Mom always said it was a good thing Pendleton made a great product because the "throw" and Monica grew old together. They are still together.*

Your MAMAs (Mothers And Many Aunts) are a cast of thousands and all of them will give you far more attention than even YOU will be able to deal with handling, so relax and enjoy yourself, but give careful consideration as to what they do, and figure out how to be a part of it. They have LOTS of interests. Don't get left behind.

Yes, vain and callow youth, I AM better looking than you are and I am WAY smarter. If YOU are to grow into something more than a dabbler, trifler, or dilettante, you need to start paying attention to your MAMAs.

It was very cold here this morning but the sun is bright now and there is no wind. Cats hate wind. Learn that in case it has not occurred to you already.

— *Your Country Cousin, Puffer*

Date; Tuesday, November 23
To: Puffer • From: Henry

Dear Puffer,

I shall find a blanket and claim it as mine. I think I have one all picked out. So far I have played cards twice (my Mom won with my help), gone to the kitty doctor three times, and lived to tell the tale. I have 200 e-mails teaching me how to be in the world, I have a Mom who has become my full-time secretary, I have explored every room, met with two of my older sisters, am meeting the third on Wednesday, and a few other things. Am I keeping up?

I already knew you were smarter than I am. Sorry to hear you are better looking. Oh, well. I am more unusual. I pay attention to my MAMAs at least half the time; too much more will make them think they are in charge, or so my friend Rhett Butler says.

I like wind. Does that mean I am not a cat? I grew up in it. It makes the leaves dance, I LOVE to chase dancing leaves. Maybe you just haven't been held right in the arms of a gentle mountain wind.

— *Your city slicker cousin, I Henry*

Date: Tuesday, November 23
To: Henry • From: Puffer

Dear I,

The trick of paying attention is to REALLY pay attention without APPEARING to do so. Study the technique. It pays off for cats with LARGE staffs to manage and you seem to be in that category.

Gentle zephyrs are not WINDS. (sigh). There is SO much you don't know ! (Your trivia lesson for the day: Zephyrus was considered by the Greeks to be the most mild and gentle of all sylvan deities).

Have to go now. I am watching Jeopardy with Mom.

— *Your Country Cousin, Puffer*

CHAPTER 14

It's Me Again, Henry

Date: Monday, November 22
To: Henry • From: Iris

Hi, Henry:

It's me, your other sister. I am sorry our sisters hurt your feelings. I guess they wouldn't play with me anymore either. Maybe.

Anyway, I was wondering if you and me could have a family reunion too. We being city kitties and all now. Mom said maybe Wednesday night after work, if it is OK with your Moms. Ask 'em and let me know.

Things are better here. I got two new brothers and a big sister. Whew, lot to learn. The orange brother has stopped hissing at me. Think I can get him to play. The other brother who kinda looks like me and is way bigger mostly ignores me. My Moms say he is "The King." We'll see. I have a big white one like your black one. She is pretty nice to me. No cuddles, though.

My Moms keep telling me what a pretty girl I am and how sweet I am. My one Mom, the blond one, is really, really goofy about me. I got her wrapped real good. The grey head one likes me pretty much, too. All in all I am sittin' pretty, as they say.

Hope I get to see you soon.

— *Your sister, Iris*

"Dear Iris: Henry will only get on your nerves. Make it a **short** *visit!"*

— Sister Gigi

Date: Monday, November 22
To: Iris • From: Henry

Hi Iris,

I would love to see you on any day. Wednesday would be fine. What time so I can rest up?

Thanks for being sorry. I guess they have a different life from mine. We just grew apart. I hear that happens.

Sounds like you landed in a pretty exciting place. Did we get lucky or what? You didn't even have to give up a paw to get there. You owe me one. I don't know what hissing is but it sounds as if it is something to be glad about it stopping. Hope you can get him to play. I don't know about the King. If I were you I would become the Queen and rule the place.

Wow, there is a big white one like my big black one. What a world this is!

You are a pretty girl. My problem is my Moms say the same thing to me. They are having a lot of trouble remembering I'M A BOY! I am trying to be patient with them.

I don't have any blond Moms but both of mine and Vicente and all my aunts are pretty goofy about me.

Take care. A bushel-full of purrs to you....

— *Henry jm*

"Gigi is correct: I call Henry 'Tripodipuss Wrecks' because he messes up everything! (He is very sweet, however, if you can put up with that.)" — Sister Kira

CHAPTER 15

Advice About Doctors

Date: Monday, November 22
To: Henry • From: Rhett Butler

Welcome back!

Well, obviously you are just learning what's what, so your old friend Rhett Butler will help you. (I have been around the block — or rather the woods — a couple of times.)

*#1. Never, **ever** go to the kitty doctor without expecting a "tidbit." Act like everything hurts, even if you are just going in for a check-up. That way, they will begin to feel guilty and bribe you. Hold out for something they call "steak." (And if they don't cut it up into small enough pieces, start choking.)*

Now, you won't be able to play this very often. Getting your stitches out was your first missed opportunity. Your second, was when your owie opened up again. Remember, Dolly may have been a little rough, but at least she CARES!

Now, on to your sisters. OK, so you may have to let go of your old relationship with them. You know how girls are. They seem to go on while we hang on to the past and weep.

So, live in the moment, and be happy that they are in a barn being warm and fed. And then be happy that your every need and whim is being taken care of.

And remember, no matter how many legs you have, you are supposed to be independent, debonair! (and, at the same time, cuddly).

You have 8 lives left. Now, get on with them.

*—Your friend,,
Rhett Butler*

PS. You look very good with the bears.
PPS. Above all, avoid snow.

Date: Monday, November 22
To: Rhett Butler • From: Henry

Dear Rhett,

I have three really smart cat consultants: you, Puffer, my country cousin, and Punkie, who is a Tripod like me. You are all so smart. You're way up there on my list. You make me laugh. I hope I soon get to go around the block. I used to be able to run around the whole woods. Today, I would settle for the block.

I sure blew an opportunity at the kitty doctor. I rolled over, pretended nothing hurt, got no treats. They did tell me I was a brave little boy and what a good kitty I was. I liked that, but now that I know there is more to get than cheap flattery you better believe I will hold out for the good stuff. Do all kitty doctors have "steak"? If not, what should I hold out for?

I know Dolly didn't mean to hurt me. She likes me. She just wanted to play. Her paws are really big. I will teach her not to paw me, but right now I just want to get along, so I go along. It is her house and it will take me a little while until I teach her that it is my house and I am letting her stay in it.

I got a letter today from my other sister who got adopted. She wants to come over to see me on Wednesday after work. I will see if she likes me. If not, that is fine. I have lots of new pals. They write to me every day, and we are making plans to get together. I am glad they are warmer than they would be outside. Mom got them a nice house and good food.

I love my life. I get cuddled a lot, played with, kissed, and fed. I feel as if I won the lottery of homes. Lucky me. My tripod friend Punkie says we should have been called Lucky Stripes. Punkie is very clever. I have to go now and get on with my 8 lives. The bears are my new friends. I liked watching the white stuff come down from the sky. Why should I avoid snow?

– Purrs, Henry jm

"I'm so sorry I hurt you, Henry. I know you'll forgive me."

Date: Monday, November 22
To: Henry • From: Rhett Butler

Dear Sir Henry:

Kitty **doctors** *DO NOT have steak! They have healthy food in tins and packages that* we all hate. *No, it is up to our mommies to broil us a nice steak, and then to cut it up into tiny little pieces as a treat. They usually do this the day of our visit to the Doctors, but it is OK if it is the night before.*

This treat should be offered if they take you OUT to have your nails clipped. (Perhaps they haven't told you about manicures, but even if you have only 3 paws to clip, it is still an ordeal.) They do this so we can walk properly, as when we were wild, we would climb trees and do things that would keep our claws trim.

But this is even better. If they do it themselves, look hurt (even though you're not) so they will give you a treat. If they take you out and a total stranger does it, look scared so that they will cook a steak for you.

Fast becoming one of your best friends.

– Mr. Rhett Butler

Date: Tuesday, November 22
To: Rhett Butler • From: Henry

Dear Rhett,

Why don't kitty doctors have steak? I thought the stuff in the tins was great. It was way better than what I had in the wild. My Mom is making a big pot of stew now. It smells really good. Want to come for dinner? Is stew as good as steak? I will see if I can have some even though I have no plan ever to go back to a kitty doctor. I will tell my Moms about the steak deal.

You always tell me things right after I have blown it. I had my nails clipped by Dr. Mom today and two weeks ago. It wasn't bad at all. Should I pretend it was bad? Dr. Mom does things really gently. I like her. She is really careful with me.

I get them to give me things because I am so cute. I now point out to everybody that I am an "M" cat. (I don't tell them that I didn't figure that out myself). Once I looked in the mirror it seemed so obvious that I was embarrassed to tell them I didn't know it myself. How could I have missed it? I am forever in your debt for pointing it out. Now, I can say things like, well as an "M" cat, I believe. . . . It just sounds so much more impressive.

I like having you as one of my best friends. Thanks for sending me your picture. I put it up in my condo.

— Purrs, Sir Henry jm

"What makes this cat purr, anyway?"

Date: Tuesday, November 22
To: Henry • From: Rhett Butler

Dear Sir Henry:

Stew can be as good as steak. It depends on if they put steak into it. If so, have them wash it off, and give you some. Forget peas.

I am happy you like food in the can. When they brought me home from North Carolina, I did also. However, learning to love steak does not mean that we give up liking food in the can. It is just that once we are adopted (and make sure you get all of your shots before you start expecting things) our Moms usually like to give us the "finer" (I guess that means steak) things in life. They don't do it often, though.

Don't worry about missing out on a treat after your nail clippings. You have thousands of nail clippings ahead of you, so you can catch up. Don't worry about them "spoiling" you. They do it for dogs, so why not us?

Your new friend,

— Mr. Rhett Butler

Date: Tuesday, November 22
To: Rhett Butler • From: Henry

Dear Rhett,

I don't know if they put steak in the stew, but Dolly liked it and it tasted good to me too. I just got a taste though. My Mom Cathy hates peas and lima beans so you will never find any of those in anything that comes out of this house.

I had some shots at the kitty doctors, I didn't like it much. It was an oweeee. I have one more shot to get next week. Maybe I will become my own doctor, what do you think?

I think I have been adopted. Dr. Mom was sure I was and my other Mom said we will see. She whispered in my ear last night that she loved me and she guessed I could stay, so I guess I must have been adopted. I have

already had two nail clippings. It didn't really hurt but I wiggled anyway. Dolly is at the groomer, whatever that is. I was told that she will come back with bows in her hair. How silly. I don't know what "spoiling" is, but I plan to have it done to me if it is good. I wish I could come and meet you but that is probably not in the cards quite yet. You are my best pal. Take care Rhett.

I send you purrrrs …

— *Love, Henry jm*

CHAPTER 16

Faith-Based Initiative

Subject: Back at the Ranch
Date: Tuesday, November 23
To: All My Friends • From: Henry jm

So, maybe if I stay here long enough, my picture will sink into the T-shirt, too!

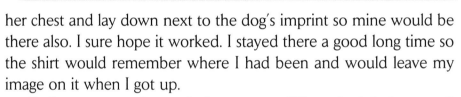

It was a very cold night. My Mom called Julian to make sure my sisters were in the barn and didn't freeze. That helped me to stop worrying about them.

I found a new wonderful place. It's called a closet. Some people live in them, so I am told. There are so many things to play with there. All the things hang down where I can bat them and play with them. There is a whole wall of something called jewelry. It is shiny and many colored and so much fun to take off the board and play with. After playing with all the jewelry I wandered over to one side of the closet. Hanging there on a pole were a zillion pieces of cloth — short-sleeved shirts, I am told. I think I heard them called T-shirts. I wonder if the "T" stands for Tripod?

Well, I was playing with all these T-shirts and I suddenly noticed they had pictures on them. Most of them had pictures of dogs. I looked and looked to find one with a picture of me. Can you believe it? With all those shirts there isn't one with a kitty like me on it! All the pictures seemed to be placed on the front right where I lie down with my Moms. I guess some dogs must have been lying a lot on my Mom's chest before I got here because they all left their pictures there.

Well, I decided that I needed to do something about that. So when I saw Mom put on one of the shirts I jumped right up onto her chest and lay down next to the dog's imprint so mine would be there also. I sure hope it worked. I stayed there a good long time so the shirt would remember where I had been and would leave my image on it when I got up.

Dolly went to a place called a groomer. When she left she was all black and woolly. When she came back she looked smaller and had bows in her ears and a scarf with birds like those I used to see in Julian. I think they are called "turkeys." She looked quite pretty. I wonder when I will go to a groomer and if they will put bows in my hair? She was very playful when she got home. My Moms tried to make sure she didn't hurt me. We rolled on the bed, I batted her with my paws, and all of a sudden I was looking into the biggest mouth I had ever seen. Dolly has great big white teeth. Her mouth is bigger than my whole head. I wasn't afraid. I will send you a picture. I call it "Faith-Based Initiative." She seemed to want to play. Her big mouth got really near my remaining front paw. I thought, *I wonder if this is a good idea? What if she decides she wants to eat my paw?* No sooner did I have the thought than she closed that very big mouth and rolled over with her paws in the air. We played some more (with our Moms hovering over us) and all was well. I will send you a picture of that very big mouth.

Mom says that I am fearless. I just think Dolly wants to be my friend. She can't help it if her paws are really big and her mouth is huge just like I can't help that I only have three paws. We are becoming friends.

I hear tomorrow is a holiday. My Moms call it Thanksgiving. They say we are having a lot of new friends over for dinner. We are having a turkey. Now, that makes me a bit nervous because up until two weeks ago flocks of turkeys were running wild with me. I can't understand why we are having one for dinner. I guess there is still much for me to learn.

Anyway, as long as there is this thing called Thanksgiving I will wish all of you a happy one. I am thankful my Moms didn't give me a permanent nap, I am thankful that I have a warm place to sleep and toys to play with and Moms that love me. I am thankful that I have three legs so I can run and play. I am thankful for all of you in my life. I know it is you that love and take care of my Moms so they can take care of me and Dolly. Thanks for being in my world.

Happy Thanksgiving!

– Henry jm

"**We're** playing, are we not?"

"This was truly a Faith-Based Initiative!"

Date: Wednesday, November 24
To: Henry • From: Puffer

Hey, I!

You are getting more handsome by the week! We look SOMETHING alike. I have a big ruff around my neck and my hair is longer. It starts out darker like yours but blends out to a very pleasing cocoa and finally burnished pale gold. In the winter it is all dark. Mom has several brushes and combs she INSISTS on using on me.

I am not a very large cat. I am dainty and feminine. I will try to get Mom to take my picture. I tried to get her attention today but she was busy baking. I'll have to make myself scarce tomorrow. Every time she does THIS much baking, a WHOLE lot of people show up and they usually have children. I am not very fond of children. I like most adults. Sometimes the people bring their dogs along because they think dogs get to run in the country. If I got to choose who came to eat I would NOT include people with dogs or children.

Puffer

Pokey goes to the groomer to get a bath and get her nails clipped. She hates the dryer so Mom has to bring her home damp. Pokey is fearless about most things but she is frightened by blow dryers. There is no accounting for dogs. Dolly must be a VERY unusual dog. She probably does NOT want to disappoint her MAMAs (mothers and many aunts), so she is trying to take you in stride. I don't know much about poodles. You are on your own where Dolly's inclinations about pleasing others and accepting you as a house mate are concerned. Good Luck!

Pokey is probably a "designer dog." The vets think she is part Catahoula and part Whippet. I'm not sure what all that means EXCEPT for the fact that it means she can RUN REALLY FAST and she NEVER tires out. Everyone thinks she is a remarkable dog. They all want to buy her. Mom says they don't have that much money. I'd sell her cheap. It was much more to my liking around here before she came to live here. I don't like to admit it — but I'll tell you

Puffer

— she DOES come in handy sometimes. NO ONE comes in the yard unchallenged. She knows when someone or something comes in the yard before Mom does AND before I do.

She is not an aggressive dog but she IS exuberant. We will never be friends, but we are learning to tolerate each other (especially if Mom is watching).

Enjoy your day tomorrow with ALL the MAMAs. You won't run out of laps all day!

Your Country Cousin,
— Puffer

Subject: Re: Closets and Teeth
Date: Wednesday, November 24
To: Henri • From: Auntie Mariam

Dear Henri,

Rajah is exceedingly fond of closets! He thinks they are safe places to hide during storms with thunder and lightening, and he always tries to drag me into one with him when he hears a loud and scary noise, like a car backfiring. He is not especially interested in my clothes, although I have a couple of nice tee shirts with his picture on them. When it is cold outside, Rajah would rather be outside than in, as he happens to be dressed for cold weather all the time. I try to accommodate him by not turning on the heat indoors until it gets very, very cold, and then I save up some of the cold to put back in the house for him in the summer.

I see in the photo that you are getting acquainted with your Mom's computer. It won't be long before you'll be able to write your own letters instead of dictating them to your secretary. There is a technique for writing on the computer called "hunt and peck," which will be relatively

"Someone said there was a mouse around here, but I can't find it!"

Date: Thursday, November 25
To: Auntie Mariam • From: Henri

Thanks for telling me the story about the teeth. I am not afraid but they do look very sharp and very big. Dolly only does that when she is playing with me so I guessed it was OK. Didn't think of looking in there for leftovers, good idea. This is my first "T" day, I am glad I don't live in the cold anymore, I like my closet, I am thankful for my feather toy, my bed, my stuffed animals, my food and all my new friends and relatives. I am a lucky stripe (teee hee) if ever I saw one.

— Henry

easy for you, since you are already a hunter. Pecking is something that birds do. If you watch them, you will quickly get the hang of it.

Do not to be afraid when Dolly opens her great big mouth full of huge white teeth. Rajah has two pug friends (they are very small dogs, about your size), and when they come over to play with him, they like to stick their heads in his mouth. Sometimes they lick his tonsils, and it makes him sneeze. Maybe they like to look around in there because there is something really interesting between his teeth, like food. At any rate, he is always very gentle with them, and doesn't growl unless they pull his whiskers. He would never hurt them, though, because he loves them.

I hope you have a nice Thanksgiving and a nice visit with your sister, Iris.

— Love, Auntie Mariam

CHAPTER 17

Happy "T" Day

Date: Thursday, November 25
To: Henry • From: Rhett Butler

Dear Sir Henry:

I should have informed you about today. Today is a day when your Mommies cook a turkey, or get invited out for one. Never mind what a turkey is, what is important is that it tastes terrific! Thanksgiving was invented by a cat a long, long, time ago to get two groups called Pilgrims and Indians to stop fighting each other. The cat figured that if everyone were full (including him), no one would fight.

So he sprayed a large ugly bird. This bird smelled so much (some people don't appreciate the smell of our spray) that a pilgrim killed it and cooked it to get rid of the odor. The cat smelled the turkey, and threatened to spray the Pilgrim unless he got a prime piece. The pilgrim gave the cat a piece, and was very thankful that the cat did not spray him. That is why today is called Thanksgiving. Mommies give us a piece of turkey, and we are good boys all day.

Your friend,

— Mr. Rhett Butler

PS. There are several other "special eating days" coming up, but I don't want to have you think about everything all at once. A warning: If your Moms bring home a big red bunch of flowers (I think they are called Poinsettias) DO NOT EAT THEM. They are not good for us, and will get us a trip either to the Vet or to the big cat in the sky.

Date: Thursday, November 25
To: Henry • From: Aunt Nikker

Hola, Henry (jm)...

Thank you for sharing your news and latest pictures. I'm pleased to note that you seem to be coming along well, that you called attention to the oversight of no kitty T-shirts, that you and Dolly are getting along well. (My! Those teeth do look sharp!)

Most of all, I'm happy that you found new moms with big hearts who will love and take care of you...because the world can be a very scary place sometimes. And if that isn't something to be grateful for this Thanksgiving, I don't know what is!

I send you soft strokes and much love from the jungle...

— Aunt Nicky

Date: Thursday, November 25
To: Aunt Nikker • From: Henry

Dear Aunt Nikker,

Where is the jungle? It sounds like a place I would like. Thanks for noting that I am coming along. It sounds as if that is a good thing to be doing. I think today is my coming-out party; I will meet many of my cor-respondents.

Speaking of big hearts: My Mom had a pet scan for her heart in a big machine of which there are just 10 in the States. She has been having pain in her chest; could be her lungs, but they decided to check it out. She was very scared. She came home with a great big smile and hugged me a long time. They said she had a very strong heart with good blood flow. I could have told her that. (sigh) Why do humans spend money on fancy tests when I know more about who has a good heart and who doesn't?

I am most thankful that I found my new life. One limb seems a small price to pay and, besides, I can do everything. I do miss out of doors. Mom says until I heal more I can't go out.

Happy "T" day.

— Your nephew, Henry jm

Date: Thursday, November 25
To: Puffer • From: Henry

Dear Puffer,

Happy "T" day. I don't know much about big black poodles. Mom says that when they lost Agatha and Beau (Jack Russell terriers),

they tried at all the shelters to get a little dog. None available. My Moms can't live without a dog for a day (although they lived a combined 131 years without a cat — *humpf!*). Mom went to the computer and typed in "poodle" and found a special breeder who lived a mile from here. They went over in a flash and brought Dolly home that night. She was my age when she came. Dolly likes

me so much she hardly leaves me alone. I don't get it. I am so little and so different from her. We will become friends. I just know it.

I think I like everybody, but then, I don't really know. I like every-body that comes to visit. My sister Iris, who lives now with Aunt Eug-enie, came over last night. She wasn't too thrilled about seeing me. Women! They just don't get it. [See next page for photos of visit.]

Dolly is faster than the wind. She goes to the ball field every day when it is still dark and runs very fast for an hour. She plays with her friends. I stay home and cuddle. I hope I don't get very large. Moms love me this size. I was playing hard yesterday and one of my stitches opened. Back to the table and glue. I don't like that.

Have a good day.

— I Henry

"Henry, what IS that noisy thing around your neck?"

He even tried asking for a scratch — and almost got it.

Exclusive Photos of Iris's Unhappy Visit with Henry

Henry tried sincerely to greet his sister, but to no avail.

"I don't wish to discuss it."

"Shouldn't _I_ be the one who's upset? I mean, it's _my_ house."

"Fine. But I can lick you any day."

Date: Thursday, November 25
To: Henry • From: Puffer

Dear I,

We use the computer a whole lot but we don't seem to be able to pick out extra animals to live here by using one. Maybe we are listed on some Web site we don't know about and people find US that way to drop off their UNWANTED animals. We have 1000 acres, so I guess we do have room. (sigh) The latest arrival is an orange and white cat and Mom's daughter-in-law decided to call her "Molly." Molly is young and has long, long rangy back legs. She has short hair. She is not wild, so someone just got tired of her, I guess. I think that is very sad. How could anyone get tired of a cat?

— Puffer

"They're makin' me do this, OK?"

"Don't come one scratch closer."

Date: Thursday, November 25
To: Henry • From: Uncle Bob

Dear Nephew Henry,

And a Happy Thanksgiving to you, from our large family in Oakland — 20 like your Moms and two small dogs, Nandi and Anabelle. Maybe you'll met them one day.

Hey, what a great line: "Faith-Based Initiative"! I think you're fearless too.

Have fun in the closet.

And on Thanksgiving and forever, live in plenty. You've got the right family for it.

— Love from Uncle Bob and Aunt Joan

"Wait a minute: Does this mean that I'm adopted, too?"

CHAPTER 18

Henry Houdini

Subject: My Thanksgiving
Date: Saturday, November 27
To: All My Friends • From: Henry

Wow, is Thanksgiving ever a neat holiday! I got petted and played with for hours. And then I got some really special treats in my dish. My friend Rhett Butler told me what treats I should ask for and it worked. I ate it all and then played for hours after my big meal. There was a lot of laughter and a lot of food. I met my Aunt Evelina and Aunt Karen, and they really liked me a lot. They said I was a special soul. I don't know what a soul is, but when they said it we looked into each other's eyes and it felt like a good thing to be. Aunt Jane took some cute pictures of me. Uncle Tim and Aunt Jamie came all the way from Oakland to see me, and today my Uncle Mike and Uncle Kevin came up from Palm Desert. I never knew there could be so many people in the universe!

I was so excited Thanksgiving night that I just didn't want to go to my compound. So, after horse Dolly was put to bed and my Moms went to bed, I decided to escape. It took me awhile because Mom Cathy had clothespins every inch holding my tent down. Well, I huffed and I puffed and I pushed and I got out. Mom heard my jingle bell in the bathroom. She was shocked. She called me a scamp and put me right back in my compound. Now, that was a lot of work for a tripod guy just to be plopped back where I started. This time she put a large cardboard scratchboard against the fence. She said, "Good night, Henry," and turned out the light. I meooowed a lot and nobody seemed to care, so I figured I had to take matters into my own

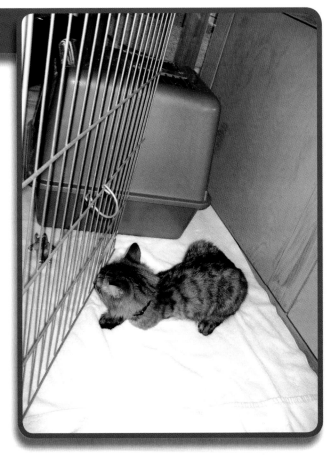

paws. I climbed on everything to re-check if I had missed an opening. No luck. But I RE-ALLY wanted to get out. So I went back to my original exit point. It was very much harder to escape the second time. The box Mom put there was heavy, and that, with the fence, was a bit much for a small fellow like me. In case you haven't figured it out yet, I am not a guy who gives up easily. So, I pushed and pushed and *meooowed* some more. Dolly chimed in, which was a useful distraction. It took much work. I almost gave up. But then, there I was, outside the compound! Victory! Henry Houdini! I walked very slowly so my bell would not tell my Moms that I was on the prowl. Then, I thought I saw something and I pounced, a proper thing for a kitty to do. Well it was nothing I could get my paw on or sink my teeth into, but the pounce made my bell to go off. Zap, Mom was out of the bed giving me another "you little scamp" lecture, and back to the clinker I went. This time she got some five-pound weights and put them on the box, and put the box against the gate. I knew it was over for me that evening. I thought with two wins on my part that she would be a good sport and let me sleep on the bed. Nope. I was very tired by then, so Dolly and I just closed our eyes and went into the land of nod. I had dreams of climbing over all obstacles and it made me just purrr.

I really like my new home. I love that you all write to me and teach me how to be in the world. I have a few gaps in learning, as the Julian woods didn't have all the rules you all have. I wonder why all of you don't just live outdoors? There is space enough for everybody and you can go wherever you want in the middle of the night. On the other paw, it is very warm and snuggly in this place called a house. (*Sigh.*) I guess I am already learning that life is filled with choices and trade-offs. All in all, I think I did pretty darn good. I am a happy boy. I think I will go lie on Dolly's fur. It is *sooooo* soft. Hope you had as good a holiday as I did.

Hugs and cuddles,

— Henry jm

Subject: Thanksgiving Photos
Date: Saturday, November 27
To: Henri • From: Auntie Mariam

Dear Henri,

Rajah was indignant when he heard that you were wearing a jingle bell around your neck. "How on earth can Henry hunt with that thing?" he wanted to know. Rajah used to have three different ID tags around his neck that clinked and jingled whenever he moved or stuck his head out the car window. One day he said to me, "Mom, how would YOU like it if something tied around your neck clattered and clinked every time you moved?" Well, I had to admit that it wouldn't be much fun, but I told him he needed to wear those tags in case he got lost. "Well," he asked, "can't you at least make them shut up so a guy has a fighting chance when he's stalking a squirrel?" I saw his point, and I wrapped them in bubble wrap with tape around it, which looks a bit odd, but at least gives both of us some peace and quiet. A few weeks later, Rajah showed his appreciation by catching a mouse in the kitchen and, er, ushering it into mousie heaven.

I think you are very resourceful to escape your compound at night, which I know is your favorite time for exploring and hunting. Once you learn to use your litter box and your leg heals, perhaps your Moms will give you the run of the house. I know you're dying to visit them when they're asleep in their beds! Although Dolly is not particularly nocturnal, I am sure she will want to share in some of your nighttime adventures. When you curl up and sleep during the day, I know you are dreaming about those adventures.

Love,

— Auntie Mariam

THE DREADED "COMPOUND"

it *trés* irritating if I take to hunting.

I don't know if I will have the run of the house. I use my litter box all of the time, I am a good boy that way. They say that they don't want me to sleep on the bed. How silly can you get? It will take me awhile but sooner or later I will get on the bed at night and have the run of the house. Dolly is a sleepykins at night. I will ask my Moms if I have to wear the bell all the time.

— *Love, Henry jm*

Date: Saturday, November 27
To: Henry • From: Punkie

Gee, Henry, it sounds like you are a very persistent, smart, resourceful fellow! Good for you for trying to escape your compound!

Maybe your Moms don't know that cats are naturally nocturnal and that we have to learn to sleep at night like the humans and the dogs do. When we are kittens we want to be up and play sometimes during the night — but as we add a few months to our age, we learn to alter our sleeping patterns. I am just two or three months older than you, and I've made the change over to sleeping at night.

It helps that Mom lets me sleep with her and the other cats. Some humans don't understand that we cats are highly social too — they think cats are solitary creatures. But we're not. We want to be close to our moms, just as the dogs do. So maybe your Moms don't understand how lonely it is to be put in a compound on the floor at night. Did you tell them that you were trying to escape so you could be with them? You should tell them, then maybe they'll understand why you are an Escape-O.

My Mom had me sleep in the bathroom for the first couple weeks I lived here, the first week because she was still trying to save my mangled leg and I was in very bad shape — high fever and all. Then, the second week because my leg got cut off and I had to recover from

Date: Saturday, November 27
To: Auntie Mariam • From: Henri

I didn't know that hunting was what I was supposed to do. I thought I was supposed to run around and play and look cute and curl up in people's laps and stuff like that. Maybe when I am bigger I will be a hunter. Dolly sleeps in a thing called a kennel. It is odd, she is so big and I am so small. My compound is a lot bigger than her kennel. Suits me fine, but it doesn't feel fair to her. I sleep right next to her kennel. I can run around but she can't.

My Moms wouldn't know where I am if I didn't have my jingle bell. I sort of like it because it feels as if it announces me. I may find

"I'll tell you what, Henry: You scratch my back and I'll scratch yours."

"That's a deal."

that. She also wanted to make sure the other cats wouldn't hurt me in the night. She gave me a heating pad in a nice warm cardboard box with a towel, but I still didn't like it. I cried and scratched at the door every night until I gave up and went to sleep. I even tore some of the molding off the door, trying to claw my way out. But the door was just too much for me.

I just wanted to be with Mom and sleep with her. It was sooooo lonely in that bathroom all by myself. I was used to sleeping with my cat-Mom and brother, so to sleep alone is a painful, lonely thing. I hated it. I'm sure you hate it too, that's why you're trying to escape all the time. Good for you, Henry! Keep at it, and maybe your Moms will see how much you want to be near them and that you don't like separation.

I wish I lived closer, then maybe you and I could have sleepovers and sleep together — then you wouldn't be lonely at night anymore.

— Bye for now, Punkie

Subject: Next up…Christmas!! • Date: Saturday, November 27
To: Henry • From: Puffer

Dear I,

Thanksgiving IS a neat holiday. The next big one is Christmas. It's even BIGGER! Remember the trees from your Julian days? Well your MAMAS (Moms And Many Aunts) bring a tree INSIDE the house! Can you believe it? It will have a WHOLE bunch of shiny stuff on it and (you'll LOVE this part)......IT IS THERE **JUST** FOR YOUR ENTERTAINMENT! Are you EVER going to love this tree!! You can climb in it and knock things off it and launch yourself at it and always remember: It is YOUR tree and it IS there JUST for you! Have fun just thinking about it!

Your country cousin — Puffer

CHAPTER 19

A Cat's Bill of Rights

Subject: Christmas
Date: Sunday, November 28
To: Puffer • From: I Henry

Puffer, I don't think my Moms are getting a tree. I heard them say they had to stop because of Beauregard, whoever he was. Now they say that I would break everything, I just don't know, if you have one I hope I get one too. We'll see.

– I Henry

Four score and seven paws ago, our forefelines said we could do pretty much whatever we want.

– Kittiesburg Address

Subject: No Tree???
Date: Sunday, November 28
To: I Henry • From: Puffer

Dear I,

No tree ??? I am SURE having a tree is in the Cat's Bill Of Rights! Surely they jest! Maybe they will surprise you with an I Henry Special Cat Tree.??? Your MAMAs (Moms and Many Aunts) are resourceful and multitalented, to say nothing of clever, AND they wouldn't WANT you to be deprived of ANYTHING on your very FIRST CHRISTMAS!

Another good thing about Christmas is STOCKINGS! The stockings get HUNG up, and then the good part is: THEY GET FILLED UP! I have my own stocking to hang up and it has MY name on it.

And PRESENTS! If SantheFan doesn't come here for Christmas, she

mails mine to me. SantheFan is my other mother and she mails me REALLY good presents all year long.

It is less than a month until Christmas. YOU need to get busy arranging for ALL the things you want! Hop to it, I!

– Puffer

Date: Sunday, November 28
To: Puffer • From: I Henry

Dear Puffer,

I didn't know there was a Cat's Bill of Rights. Where can I get a copy? I don't think they jest, I think that they don't have a tree anymore, they decorate the house in different ways. Since I have never been here I don't know what other ways. Maybe they will get me a cat tree.

I haven't seen any stockings yet either. Maybe my family doesn't know about such things.

I think I have everything I want, but I will give it some thought. I might be wrong about that. I am sure you can help me with the "Things I can't live without, thank you" list. You are pretty smart for a country cousin. It sounds as if you have trained them all well.

My Moms and I are having a bit of a struggle about who is training whom. They have a bell around my neck. I don't like it much, and I think it will interfere with my hunting. They say it is so they can find where I am. What if I don't want to be found? If I make a move, it jingles. I have to think about this one. Is there something in the Cat's Bill of Rights that outlaws bells?

– I Henry

"What the—? This really is something new if I can't decide what part to break first!"

Subject: A Cat's Bill of Rights
Date: Sunday, November 28
To: Henry • From: Puffer

Dear I,

Gracious! Of COURSE there is a Cat's Bill of Rights! #1 is Staff Acquisition: Cats get to choose with whom they live. (You've done yourself proud with that one.) We'll work on the other ones as the need arises, but as I recall, Christmas Trees are a subCATegory under #2, which is Living Arrangements.

How big is your enclosure? Large enough for a "cat tree"? Carefully watch the decorations they put up around the house, and if you see something you covet, just relocate it to "your" tree as a decoration.

If your MAMAs don't put up Christmas stockings for you and Dolly with your names on them, you should do what comes naturally: Sit on their laps, look into their eyes, concentrate, purr softly and HYPNOTIZE them into thinking it is THEIR idea. (A variation on this might work for the tree: Get them to believe that they need a living tree this year so they can replant it somewhere in Julian as reforestation.)

The bell is part of #3: Privacy and Freedom to Move About As Desired. You have some choices here, and success will depend on the tools you have at your disposal. For example, you said Dolly had teeth. Could you trust her to bite off the bell? What kind of food do

"Yes, you will look deeply into my eyes and do what I want."

"You will release me from my compound. Oh yes, you will...."

you have to eat? Anything you could drag it through and clog it up so it wouldn't do a Lily Tomlin imitation (one ringy dingy, two ringy dingies)? Are your back legs strong enough to pull it over your head? Is the collar rigid or elasticized? Elasticized ones are a snap to remove. (Remember my telling you about Monica Mellow and the harnesses? She "lost" so many collars that Mom gave up on them and went to a harness, but only when she was going on a leash somewhere.)

For now, think about what YOU want and I'll try to help you figure out a way to mesmerize them into DOING it — MMAMMAs (Mesmerized Moms And Many Mesmerized Aunts).

—Puffer

Date: Sunday, November 28
To: Puffer • From: I Henry

Dear Puffer,

I am indeed a lucky boy to have such a smart country cousin. I was a country cat and I didn't know any of the things that you seem to know. I may include your sections in my next letter as I am afraid that there are many cats and kittens that have no idea what their feline rights are. We all have very liberal-minded moms, so I assume that these former civil rights people will fight for our rights as soon as I inform them of what they are. I love having a name that includes absolutely everybody, MMAMMAs is just perfect. How long did it take you to learn all the stuff you know? It makes my head swim.

Mom Cathy already conceded that I won the night battle. No more tent. When Dolly goes to bed I get to roam where I want to. Auntie Mariam in Philly tells me I shouldn't have to wear a bell. She says my hearing is 300 times what my Moms hear, and it bothers my ears. I don't like it very much; I just thought it came with the territory. Mom is thinking about taking off my collar at night so I can roam silently. She says that is a *compromise*, whatever that means. All in all, I am feeling like a pretty lucky boy. My Moms both love me. One of my Moms ordered a special vest for Christmas for my other Mom. It is a secret but it has cats on it. Soon there will be pictures of me around.

Thanks for being such a smart cat and taking the time to tutor me. I am in your debt

— I Henry

Date: Sunday, November 28
To: I Henry • From: Puffer

Dear I,

We cats have passed on an oral history. Everything I know, I learned from Monica Mellow WMBC (World's Most Beautiful Cat, who lived to be 23). I've told you about her. We have an OBLIGATION to pass on what we have learned, so you should feel free to pass on what you think other cats need to know. There is no "ownership" or "copycatrights." Other cats out there may know things that WE don't know! (Improbable, but a possibility.....tee hee.) We NEED to share!

CATS OF THE WORLD, UNITE.....CAST OFF YOUR BELLS!! (See how fast this works?? You seem to have come up with a compromise ALREADY thanks to a MAMA in Philly. She probably has been mesmerized and is, in fact, a MMAMMA). This computer-assisted sharing IS to our advantage. Worked for you!

No debt involved, I. Obligation to spread the word to the willing who will listen, yes! Don't be disappointed if you find some who don't know how to listen, ask questions, learn and share. That is their loss (it is NOT a CATastrophe).

– Puffer

Subject: CATastrophe
Date: Sunday, November 28
To: Puffer • From: I Henry

Dear Puffer,

I think we cats do better than our humans. Sometimes the TV is on in my room and there is a thing called news. People are going bang, bang, and then get lawyers for something called their "rights." They seem to think that there is not enough of everything to share. How silly they are. Maybe that is why they have us.

I am glad there are no copycatrights, otherwise you wouldn't have learned everything from Monica Mellow WMBC and then I wouldn't have learned it from you. My friend Rhett Butler, in LA, is a pretty smart cat. So Is Punkie, who lost a back leg, so she will never be as good a jumper as I am.

It seems to me that it would be a CATastrophe if someone didn't want to share and learn. I am going to learn to be a really good teacher, after I tame my Moms and all the MMAMMAs and, of course, Dolly.

– I Henry

Subject: CATastrophe
Date: Sunday, November 28
To: I Henry • From: Puffer

Dear I,

Rhett Butler and Punkie sound interesting. You have managed to capture the attention of quite a group! Good for you!

Monica Mellow, WMBC, never believed that EVERYONE would "believe"… as long as some MAY, it is NOT a CATastrophe and that is why we should continue to try.

– Puffer

CHAPTER 20

I Won!

Date: Monday, November 29
To: All My Friends • From: Henry jm

I am *soooo* excited. As you all know, I don't like sleeping in my compound, even though it is only two feet from the bed. I can see the bed and I want to be *on* the bed. Dolly seems to be more compliant than I plan to be. She grudgingly goes into her kennel every night. Sometimes she gives a growl, just to let my Moms know that she doesn't want to go, but, in the end, she goes — growl and all.

Well, two nights ago when they had put the dreaded sheet up (that is what keeps me from escaping), I was determined that I could and would get out, this time for good. I watched carefully as Mom put all the clothespins on, pinning the sheet onto the gate. As the last one went "SNAP" I thought: "This is a CATastrophe, and this is the last night this is going to happen!"

I waited until everybody was in bed with lights out. I then climbed up on top of my litter box to the next level. It seemed that if I pushed off hard I could fly into the dreaded sheep sheet and make the clothes pins snap. I wasn't quite sure where I would land but it was only about three feet up so I figured I would be OK. I did it once and I heard one pin go snap but still no way out. I made a thump and Mom turned on the flashlight to see what on earth I was doing. I decided to do it a second time, no luck.

The third time I hurled myself in the air with all the force of my four-pound body and a whole bunch of the pins snapped off. Mom watched with amazement and knew that she had been had. She had such admiration for my valiant efforts. Plus she was so worried that I might kill myself trying that she took down the dreaded sheet for good and said, "OK, Henry, you win, no more sheet." Well, I beamed with pride, ran right up to the bed, curled up by my Mom and celebrated with a cat-nap.

I have some very smart friends out there that are teaching me how to be in my world. My country cousin Puffer told me how to sit and stare into my Mom's eyes so they will do what I want and think it is their idea. Puffer says I can do it with everybody. He came up with a word for all of you that I really like: MMAMMAs (Mesmerized Moms And Many Mesmerized Aunts). So I am practicing. Puffer said that I needed to get ready for Christmas and the tree and stockings. I heard my Moms don't do a tree anymore because of the dog and now because of me. Puffer was aghast and told me I was to follow the Cat's Bill of Rights and quickly get my Moms into shape. I didn't know where to find such a bill. He says that we cats have passed on an oral history forever and we have an obligation to pass on what we know to younger kitties.

I'm not sure what I would do without Puffer, Rhett Butler, Punkie, and all my MMAMMAs and Uncles. They are good teachers. So I am working on the tree and the stocking. My Auntie Mariam in Philly got me to negotiate to get my silly bell off. It bothers me and will interfere with my hunting. Last night I had no collar, no bell, no tag I was free as a bird. I slept on the bed, ran around at night, had a snack in the wee early hours of the morning. It was the BEST night I ever had in my whole life. I think this is the way it is going to be from now on. Fight for your needs, leap, and the net will appear. It worked for me, so I am passing it on to all of you.

— *Henry jm*

Subject: You Did It!
Date: Monday, November 29
To: Henry • From: Iris

Dear Henry-

Yahoo! You did it. I knew you would. So did my Moms.

I'll tell you, Henry, you just gotta stick to it. You can't give up. You know what's right. No way you should sleep in your compound. Your place is on the bed, a mom by your side, or wherever you want to sleep.

Mr. K. (he's my really big brother here and he knows LOTS of important stuff) said one of the rules (I don't know which number it is) is Cats Always Have Right of Way in Sleeping Wherever. That's what he said. I know it is true. My Moms thought I should stay in the room for a way long time. Well I didn't think so.

All you gotta do is look up at them, meow just a teeny bit, and don't blink. They can't hold up to that and you can get anything you want.

"Look, Moms! No bell, no collar. I'm free!"

Well next thing I knew I had the run of the house, and I was sleeping on my blonde Mom's head. Throw in a little purr and it's all over for them.

I am sorry I was so grumpy the other night when I came to visit. I wanted to see you and then I got scared in that big house. Strange smells. So I guess I growled at you. I am sorry if I hurt your feelings. I am really glad you got such a good place, good moms and all. That's the best. I know.

— Your sister, Iris

Date: Monday, November 29
To: Henry • From: Punkie

Henry,

You are such an inspiration to me! Wow! You're my hero! I am so impressed with how you can fly out of your compound — right through the sheet/roof! Amazing!

I like that hypnotizing part too…I will have to try it with my Mom and see if it works on her.

I have a bell on my collar — Mom says she likes to know where I am in the house. But it is elastic and I have managed to get it off lots of times already. I've chewed my collar all up in the process. It's all rag- gedy. Mom goes looking for it and sooner or later she finds it and puts it back on me. I wonder if I can get the dog to eat it?

The other cats all have bells too, because Mom says it gives the birds a fighting chance. But I only have one hind leg and I can't jump and catch birds anyway, so why do I have to wear a bell? I notice that the other cats keep losing their collars too. They go out in the morn- ing with a collar and come back at night naked. Mom doesn't go all around outside looking for their collars — she just buys new ones. But since I am not a threat to the birds, maybe I can hypnotize her into letting me go naked. Yup, the big bed is definitely the place to be. Our Moms may not have fur, but they're still plenty warm to sleep with. Sometimes I sleep in the curve between Mom's hip and her shoulder when she sleeps on her side. Sleeping on her is even better than the heating pad because the heating pad doesn't have a heartbeat. Sleep- ing on Mom gives me the warmth AND the heartbeat …. just like when I used to sleep with my cat Mom.

We cats move around too … we change places on the bed throughout the night … though we all kind of have our favorite places. Lion King likes to sleep like a halo over the top of Mom's head .. Max likes to sleep on the six inches between Mom and the edge of the bed. He's a high-strung edgy cat, so it makes sense he would like the edge. Some- times I pounce on him when he's sleeping and he screams and makes a big fuss, waking everybody up. It makes Mom mad when I do that ….. but Max is such an easy target, I can't help myself. A couple times Mom got so mad she made me sleep in the bathroom again, all by myself. Boy, I hated that. I am trying to learn not to pick on Max, since Mom loves him and it makes her mad Scooter and Max sometimes bat at Fannie, just to remind her that we cats have claws. They taunt her with, "Dogs drool — cats rule!" I think they're mean to Fannie, but I stay out of it. None of my business.

You said your Moms don't do a tree anymore because of the dog and now because of you. I heard my Mom say the same thing! What is it with these moms? I'm going to try Puffer's technique and see if it works…. I'm going to mesmerize my Mom into getting a tree and decorating it with nothing but cat toys, dog toys, bundles of catnip, and fun unbreakable toys for all us animals here in the house (the rabbits outside in the hutch are on their own).

— Hugs, Punkie

Subject: Freedom
Date: Monday, November 29
To: Henri • From: Aunti Mariam

Dear Henri,

As I may have mentioned, the training of humans takes considerable patience, humor, and charm. You seem to have an abundance of all three, so it seems likely that your MMAMMAs will continue to live up to your expectations, and that there will be no more CATastrophes involving bells, sheets and clothespins.

By the way, you'd better not mention the Cat's Bill of Rights to Dolly, or she'll start demanding equal rights for dogs. The next thing you know, she'll be pushing you out of bed at night and spoiling your stealth attacks on the local mouse population.

Love,

— Auntie Mariam

Subject: Advice for Dolly (the big black horse)
Date: Monday, November 29
To: Dolly • From: Eleanor and Sarah

Dear Dolly:

We believe you've been co-opted by that new feline type that has moved in. I think you'd better take some lessons from us on maintaining a cat-free home. Of course, we don't really have to worry about a cat moving in on us because Mama Phyllis is allergic to cat hair and cat dander. BUT — we've had lessons at Auntie Kilulu's like we told you before. So — take it from us — cats are to be avoided at all costs if you want to maintain good Dog Credentials. AND — it seems to us that you are getting short shrift where Mama Attention is concerned. Don't say we didn't warn you!

Looking out for your best interests,

Eleanor & Sarah

CHAPTER 21

Room for Us All

Date: Tuesday, November 30
To: Henry • From: Emmy Lu

Dear Henry,

*M*y Mom was gone for a whole week and I had to wait until she got back before I could read all your letters and see your neat pictures. She left a friend of hers here with us to house sit, and she wasn't any fun at all.

I'm glad to see that your owie is healing so nicely. I can't imagine what it would be like to have only three paws, but I'm sure I would adapt if that were ever to happen to me. My Mom loves me and my brothers and sisters very much. We don't have a big black horse like Dolly, but I have a black and tan shepherd — that's a dog — and a little mutt dog to play with sometimes. Sometimes the mutt dog chases me down the hallway and it's lots of fun 'cause I can dive under things to hide from her. You must learn to do that, too. Keep looking for places to hide under that Dolly can't come in to get you. It's lots of fun playing with them that way.

I go on adventures out in the garage because my Mom doesn't let any of us cats go outside. We all have to stay inside and amuse ourselves. We have a big house and there are lots of places to sleep and hide, and we also know how fun closets can be. My brother, Newby, lives in my Mom's closet. He is very spooky and doesn't like people too much. He loves my Mom and lets her touch him, but he doesn't let anyone else see him. We call him our "closet dweller" because he mostly comes out at night. My other brother, Weeds, is all black and very, very fat. He weighs 23 pounds, so we littler critters have to be careful that we don't get in his way. If he were to sit on us we would be mashed! He's very nice though, but because he's so fat he doesn't do much. Mostly he just lies around on the furniture and eats. My newest sister, Sissy, came to us because her other Mom couldn't keep her anymore. She's very mean sometimes, and Mom still has to have her claws taken out so she doesn't hurt the rest of us. Sissy is getting better about playing with me but I don't like it when she gets mean, so then my Mom gets after her to stop it. She's better now than when she first got here, though. My Mom loves me the best of all. She calls me the "love of her life." She tells me I'm pretty all the time and that I'm a good girl. She rescued me from the Humane Society. That's a place where people take animals that they don't want anymore. Mom doesn't go there very often because she wants to bring everyone home and that would cause a huge problem. My Dad loves animals, too, just as much as Mom. We are all very blessed to have such wonderful parents.

EMMY LU

Take good care of yourself and keep having such wonderful fun exploring neat things in the world. Just always remember: Where there's a will, there's a way, and it sounds as though you are having great fun figuring that out.

Love,

— Emmy Lu

Date: Tuesday, November 30
To: Emmy Lu • From: Henry jm

Dear Emmy Lu,

It sounds as if you have a lot of critters living there. Wow, what fun!

I have such a full mail box, it is just amazing. I didn't know anyone but my sisters, and now I have lots of friends. Thanks for the pictures.

I can't even remember having four legs. I do just fine with three, and everybody thinks I am so cute. They are surprised at how fast I can run. I will have to remember to duck under things so Dolly doesn't get me. She can run really fast, too.

Take care,

— Henry jm

Subject: A Package
Date: Tuesday, November 30
To: Punkie • From: Henry jm

Dear Punkie,

You can imagine my excitement when a package came for me. I danced around and jumped for joy and got my Mother to open it pronto. And there was that wonderful cat that just happens to match

my bedspread. Do you mind if I call it Punkie? I rolled around with it, on it, under it, and then Mom came in with her camera. She has been sick for the last 36 hours, so I have been playing fur nurse. She put on her cat T-shirt and it made me feel so at home. I was disappointed that even though I lay on several of the shirts my image

didn't stay on any of them. So now I can look at one that has all those cats on it. As if that weren't enough, then came the refrigerator pin. Christmas came early in my house and it all came my way. Very special indeed. It means a lot to me to have kitty friends because my Moms are dog people and they are not quite sure what kittens are all about. Thanks for being my friend, thanks for sharing such special things with me, and thank your Mom for throwing it really hard so it got to my front door.

– Love, Henry jm, your friend

Date: Tuesday, November 30
To: Henry • From: Punkie

Dear Henry,

Wow, that was fast! Mom just sent the package yesterday. I'm glad you like all the stuff we sent. I figured we have so much cat stuff in this house that we should share with you…especially when I read how sad you were about all the dog T-shirts. This way there will be a cat T-shirt in your Mom's closet so you will feel more at home in there. She doesn't have to wear it if she doesn't want to — we really sent it for you.

Glad you like the chenille cat too — doesn't she just look like a nice cuddly mom-cat? We thought you would like her. And the cat

'frigerator pin — well that message is especially true of you, since you are definitely not an ordinary cat! I think you are a Super Cat, since you can fly. You don't even need a cape or anything, you just take off and fly. Faster that a speeding bullet, more powerful than a choo choo train, able to leap tall compounds in a single bound — it's a bird, it's a plane, it's Super Cat!

Woo hoo! What a guy! Glad you like your presents. My Mom says it's nice for us to share things with our friends, and I see what she means. It feels good inside to share with you. Warm feline feelings. prrrrr

G'night, Henry — Punkie

CHAPTER 22

Cat Massages

Date: Wednesday, December 1
To: Punkie • From: Henry jm

Dear Punkie, I am calling my new cat Punkie, if that is OK with you. I slept with her all night. It was nice. Sometimes I sleep under her, sometimes beside her. Everybody comes in and says how cute I am when we are snuggled.

Mom Cathy is ill. I entertained her for part of the night. It is one of my new jobs, to take care of those in bed.

Mom loves the T-shirt. It is too cold to wear it today, but soon it will be warmer I have a feeling being supercat may have been how I got hurt. I don't actually remember, but I am sure I was running or hurling myself somewhere. Flying is actually quite fun. It is the landing part that can be a little tricky. Anyway, sharing is where it's at. There is much too much new stuff in the world. We need to take care of the things we have, share the stuff we have, and tend to the animals already born, like you and me. Take care, Punkie.

– *Snuggles, Henry jm*

Date: Wednesday December 1
To: Henry jm • From: Punkie

Henry; I'm glad you're taking good care of your Mom while she's sick. Please give her some purring from me.

I pretty much hang out on the bed a lot too. Mom does some of her writing there – this morning she was writing some poems for her new book. She wears a fuzzy bathrobe and I cuddle up close and knead her just like I did my cat Mom. It's a cat massage. I tell ya, a mom in a fuzzy bathrobe is about as good as it gets! Try giving your Mom a massage and see if it helps her get well.

Bed duty is an important part of being a good cat. My Mom says that sleeping with animals is the best part of having them! Soft fur, warm body, thump, thump, heartbeat.

Fannie the dog likes to go in the car and travel with Mom, but we cats don't. We like our home turf, since we are territorial critters. We get very attached to people and to places – but we don't like to go traveling around with our people. OK, gotta go now. I think I heard the can opener. . . .

– *purrrr, Punkie I (your new cat can be Punkie II, tee hee)*

"I guess my little massage did work. Mom is fast asleep."

"My job is done here. Now, what can I get into?"

I did fine in the car before my surgery. Now I am not so sure about it. I will probably get used to it, or I will be left home on the week ends. I think I prefer to get used to it. Snuggles and Purrs

– Henry jm

Date: Wednesday, December 1
To: Henry jm • From: Punkie

Oh my gosh! I totally forgot that it's your FRONT paw that's missing! That will make cat massages a bit of a challenge. Hmmmm .... but I bet you still remember how. Think back to when you were a tiny kitten with your cat mother. When you would suck on those little knobs she has on her tummy and warm, sweet milk came out ... remember that? Well, I'll bet you also remember giving her cat massages with your tiny front paws – it's instinctive, no one has to teach us how to do it, Mother Nature made it automatic. We knead our cat Mom's fur right around the area of those milky knobs and it helps the milk flow better. Do you remember doing that? Sure you do, I bet.

Well, we never give up those cat massages, even when we leave our cat moms – we just give those massages to our new moms instead. It's kind of a way of expressing love and connection.

But getting back to the massages: Since you have only your right front paw, it will be harder to give cat massages, but I'll bet you still do it, even though you may not even realize it. So, I guess you'll just have to practice so you can give one-paw massages. I bet your Mom will love it anyway. Humans love to be kneaded!

– Love, Punkie I

Date: Wednesday, December 1
To: Punkie I • From: Henry jm

Dear Punkie I:
Punkie II and I are doing our best to take care of Mom. She doesn't like to rest much so she is usually doing something or other. I will have to learn how to do a cat massage, I am not sure I know how but I will try. This is the third night since I took my leaps that I have been allowed to sleep where ever I want. I spent some of it with Mom and some of it with Punkie II. I really like her. I am so little. I am a bit afraid that one of my Moms might roll over and squish me when I am asleep. Should I put a bell on them so I have fair warning?

Date: Wednesday, December 1
To: Punkie • From: Henry jm

Dear Punkie,

Forgetting my front paw is gone isn't as bad as my forgetting that you are a girl. I was so embarrassed. What is a boy to do if I have never been able to see and sniff to find out myself. These silly computers don't give me the smells that would allow me to not make such clumsy mistakes.

I sort of remember giving Mom little massages with my tiny paws. It is now coming back. There was a rhythm to it between the one paw and then the other. It is harder to do it with only one front paw because I would push with one and stabilize with the other. I will try and see how it works, or figure out some new little ritual.

I love Punkie II. I curl up in her arms or legs, or under her, or on top of her, and fall asleep. Mom keeps coming in and telling me how cute I am and snaps another picture. She found me lying on my new shirt, which is a little big for me, but I will let my Moms wear it. It matches my color and I love that it came from your house. Mom says that your Mom was looking for a husband. Why would she want one of those when she has all of you? Sometimes it is hard to figure out moms. If she gets one he has to understand where he is in line, that is at the end. After all, you have been there and already have proved your unconditional love credentials. Humans love to be needed, sometimes they forget that it is just nice to be wanted and be kneaded in the cat sense. I got a really big treat tonight. Mom put a little tuna in with my kitty food. I am not wild about my kitty food, so I haven't been eating it all. I guess that gave her the idea to sweeten the pot. That was the idea. Got to go take care of Mom. I hope that tonight she gets some sleep so I am not on duty all night. Dolly just goes to her kennel and that is the end of her. That leaves me to do all the major purring and healing.

Night, Punkie.

— Henry jm

"You're a real doll, but just a bit too needy at times!"

CHAPTER 23

Healing Quickly

Date: Friday, December 3
To: All My Friends • From: Henry jm

Now that my wounds from my amputation are healing very well, I am a ball of energy. After I take my power naps I have periods of frenzy during which I run all over the house seeing if I can incite Dolly to chase me. When she does, she is told, "No," and made to halt. I guess our Moms aren't so sure that we can work it out ourselves. I don't think Dolly would hurt me, and if she did I would meow really loud and bat her and tell her to stop. We animals are smart that way.

I got a new job this week; I became a fur nurse. Mom Cathy has been sick all week so she didn't have much energy. I lay on her chest and purred and tried to cure her. When she was up all night I tried to entertain her and distract her. I think I did a pretty good job.

I now have something new to look forward to: the postman. I never knew it could be an important event until the postman came and brought me cards and presents. Well, I think that little red, white and blue truck is really the cats meow. My Aunt Leie sent me my first present — a cat pin — which I really like. Punkie, also a tripod, sent me my second one. She felt bad that I no longer had my sisters with me and that all the T-shirts in the closet had dogs on them. Despite the fact that I lay down on all of them, they still had only pictures of dogs. Well, Punkie sent me a wonderful chenille cat that I snuggle with all the time. She also sent a T-shirt that is way too big for me but fits my Moms. It has a bunch of cats on it and it says to adopt one of us. Well, I curl up with Punkie II and sit on my T-shirt and it makes my self-esteem *cata*-pult to the ceiling. I think I have the best cat friends, aunts, uncles, and

tutors in the whole world. I am starting to feel as if the car that bumped me did me a really big favor. It is funny; sometime the things we think are the very worst things that could ever happen to us turn out to open wonderful opportunities that would otherwise never have happened.

Today there were boxes in the living room with lots of fun stuff to play with. I think they are Christmas decorations. I can't wait to get my little paw into all of it. I will tell you more as we unwrap all the goodies. Until then snuggle with someone you love and let them know you love them.

– Henry jm

Date: Friday, December 3
To: Henry jm • From: Puffer

Dear I,

I was reading your third paragraph with interest. Some time ago I suggested to you that you were not where you are because of AN ACCIDENT. Maybe you are beginning to come around and BELIEVE me when I try to tell you something !

– Puffer (your FEMALE Country Cousin)

Dear Henry,

I'm so happy that you are healing and have so much energy. You're also right that Dolly wouldn't hurt you. Chu Chu (the mutt dog) that likes to chase me wouldn't hurt me either. We have our own animal rules and sometimes people don't understand them. Especially 'cause your Moms are more used to dogs than cats. I'm so happy that you are in their world and they are in yours. You are a very lucky little boy.

How fun to get presents! My Mom brings us presents sometimes when she goes shopping. I have my favorite thing though and Mom calls it my "fuzzy." It looks just like a mouse and I can throw it in the air and chase it all around. Sometimes it goes under things and then it's fun to reach my paw in there and try to get it out. It's a really fun toy and I would be happy to send you one if I had your address. Every kitty should have a "fuzzy" of their own.

We won't have decorations to play with this year 'cause our Dad isn't home. He is very far away in the military. When he isn't here Mom doesn't decorate anything. So we just entertain ourselves in the closets and out in the garage (there's lots of cool stuff to climb on out there) and play with all our other toys.

I'm going to send you a picture of something I like to do when my Mom washes clothes. When she brings the clothes in and puts them on the bed to fold I like to hide in them. They are all warm and toasty and it's nice to take a nap like that. Maybe you can learn how to do that too. Thank you for the letter Henry. I always look forward to hearing from you. Getting your letters makes my day much brighter. Have a happy holiday season and enjoy all your new "discoveries."

— Fondly, Emmy Lu

Dear Emmy Lu,

All my new cat friends seem to be as lucky as I am to have swell homes. I don't know what the military is but if it keeps your Dad away from home that is not good and makes me feel very sad for all of you. I hope he is OK. Tell your Mom that decorations are good for one's spirit, whether everybody is at home or not. After all, you and Chu Chu and Sissy and the rest are well worth putting up decorations for.

I didn't know I had an address. I just figured Punkie's Mom threw my toy all the way in the air until it landed on my doorstep. I asked Mom, and she said, of course we have an address. My old address was just Woods, Julian, but nobody ever sent me anything there.

— Henry jm

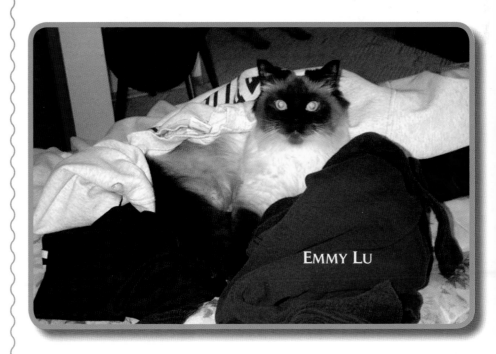

CHAPTER 24

Weeds

Subject: A Picture of Weeds
Date: Saturday, December 4
To: Henry jm • From: Emmy Lu

Dear Henry,

My Mom had an opportunity to take a picture of the biggest cat in the house this morning. Thought you might like to see what Weeds looks like. Mom tells me that he got his name Weeds 'cause when he was very, very small (only a few weeks old) my Dad and Mom rescued him out of some weeds and blackberry bushes. He was very, very sick and could fit in my Dad's hand when they got him. Mom and Dad nursed him back to health and now he weighs 23 pounds. Mom says he's too fat and she calls him "Fatty." Dad says not to call him that 'cause it will hurt his feelings. Funny thing is that when Mom says, "Hi, Fatty" he knows she's talking to him. Guess he really doesn't care what she calls him as long as she keeps the food dish full. Anyway, thought you might like to see what one of the other members of our feline household looks like. Weeds is a very mellow cat and he sleeps with Mom. He's very possessive of her when she's in bed and he will hold her hand and touches her face very softly with his paw. Dad says he has a "thing" for Mom — whatever that means. I don't understand it all, I just know that when Weeds is on the bed with Mom I don't get up there.

Mom is still sick but says that as soon as she can go shopping she will get your fuzzy and mail it to you. I told her she could send one of

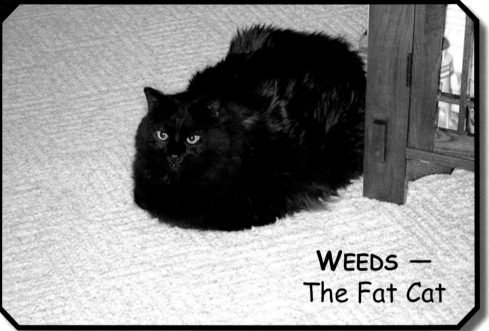

WEEDS —
The Fat Cat

mine but she said you needed a new one. I don't know why exactly 'cause mine is already broken in. But whatever Mom says goes, so you will have a brand new one for your very own.

Have a good weekend.

– Fondly, Emmy Lu

Date: Saturday, December 4
To: Emmy Lu • From: Henry jm

Dear Emmy Lu:

Wow, I never ever saw such a big cat in my whole life! I didn't know we came in those kind of sizes. I think I agree with your Dad. There is enough cruelty in the world, we don't need to call each other hurtful names. Weeds is a fine name; somehow "Fatty" doesn't feel so good. I chose my name as Henry instead of Tripod because I wanted my name to be about me, not a part of me that seems to be missing.

I am afraid that I don't know anymore than you do about what having a "thing" for someone is. WE will have to put the word out to other cats to tell us. Weeds should share with you and let you come on the bed too. It is good that you are all there to take care of your Mom when your Dad is away on a big ship. She probably needs purring and cuddling. It is hard when you come to love someone and then they go away. I wonder why people do that? Everybody should stay home all day and play with the people and animals they love. One of my Moms is retired so she is always here and my other Mom works just some of the time and she works in the back yard. I hope to get out there sometime.

I heard a story that made me really sad today. Over a year ago, before I was born and before the big fire in California, there were six feral cats born in the barn on my Mom's country property. They got them all placed in nice homes. One of them was placed with the wonderful woman who takes care of my Moms, me, Dolly and the house and garden. His name was Oliver. Little Oliver got hit by a car, like I did, only he didn't live. I think they should outlaw cars. They kill animals (and people too). I feel bad for the kitty and the kids who loved him.

Gee, both of our Moms are sick. That is no fun at all. I don't need anything in the whole world. I have people and things to play with. Tell your Mom she doesn't have to get anything new. Broken in things are better, besides they have interesting smells when oth-

OLIVER

ers have played with them.

Thanks for the pictures of Weeds. Tell your Mom to decorate the house for all of you, and then again when Dad comes home. One can never have too many decorations to bat around.

– Purrs and snuggles, Henry jm

Date: Saturday, December 4
To: Henry jm • From: Emmy Lu

Dear Henry,

Thank you for the lovely long letter. My Mom wishes she could retire so she could stay home with all of us, but it doesn't look like that will happen any time soon. You are very lucky that you have two moms and they take such good care of you.

Mom says she won't call Weeds "Fatty" any more. She didn't do it to be mean, just to tease him. He's such a loveable old guy anyway. It's OK that I don't get on the bed when Weeds is up there. I have my own little place underneath my Mom's headboard and I stay nice and toasty warm there. I can hear her when she starts waking up and then I come out from my "bed" place and sit on her slippers. Then she reaches over and gives me love and then she gets up. It all works out OK.

Your story about Oliver is very sad. That's why my Mom doesn't let any of us go outside. She doesn't want us to get hurt on the street. She says that sometimes cars can't see us and when they can't see us they hurt us really bad. Mom would be devastated if any of us got squished by a car. We don't know any better though 'cause we've always grown up in the house. One time I snuck outside when Mom wasn't looking. I thought "yippee I'm free!" but soon found out it was really scary out there. Mom didn't even know I was outside and I was getting very scared so I found one of the windows and kept pounding on it until Mom heard me. She about had a cow! She opened the door, scooped me up and gave me love and scolding all at the same time. I thought she was going to squish me to death because she held on to me so hard. Anyway, after that I decided that all my adventures would be done in the house or in the garage. None of the doors to the outside world are left open so I'm safe in my own little world. And sometimes if the door is left open for briefly, I just sit there and look out but I won't go out there ever again.

Have fun, Henry. And Henry is a fine, fine name. Adding the "jm" gives you an air of aristocracy. I don't have a title, but my Mom calls me by lots of different names – she calls me Loolie, Emmy, MeeMee. my little beauty, her long lost love (I guess she calls me that one cause when she comes home from work I run down the hall to meet her). My Mom is kind of silly when it comes to the furry side of the family. She has pet names for everyone. And we all know we are loved very much. Just as you are.

Have fun tonight. Enjoy your newly found nightly freedom.

Purrs to you,

— Emmy Lu

Dear Emmy Lu,

My Moms are OPs (older people). Mom Cathy started a thing called Real Women Project (www.realwomen.org), which is all about body image. That is why she is sensitive about the word "fatty." If you go to the Web site you will see one of the things my Mom did.

It sounds as if you all have worked out where each has their place and everybody is happy with it. That is good.

My Moms don't want me to go out either because they don't want me to get hurt anymore than I already have been. My Moms would be devastated if anything happened to either Dolly or me. They are real animal lovers. They never wanted a cat, but here I am and they love me.

I think I have an outdoor gene. Since I lived in the mountains for the first four months I just love the wind in my fur and the smells of nature. There are many people who come and go here and Dolly has an open door out the garage to go to her side yard. Mom says, there is no way I won't get out sooner or later. They just hope I have become such a cushy cat that I won't want to stay there. I think I will be OK, but there is a lot I don't know. You are a smart cat to know your limits.

Running without my jingle bell at night is really fun, just me and my body. Have a good night!

— Henry jm

Date: Saturday, December 4
To: Henry jm • From: Emmy Lu

Dear Henry,

You know, you may have an outdoor gene but it is best that you stay indoors and be an indoor boy. My brother Newby came to us from out of the park and he was about 4 months old and very wild. He had been dumped in the woods when he was little and didn't know much about people. I think he thought they were all mean and he is still

pretty spooky. He's the one that lives in Mom's closet. But Mom and Dad took him in and gave him food, water and shelter and now he lives indoors all the time. I don't think he would go back outside if given the chance. Listen to your Moms and stay indoors. We cats have our own bathroom in Mom's back bathroom and sometimes we are all in there at once – even Mom! Makes life interesting. And catboxes

aren't that bad. At least there's only one of you - there's four of us!

I will check out your Mom's Web site. My Mom is sorry that she offended her. She would never do anything to hurt anyone's feelings. She cares equally about everyone.

Go run and play now.

Hugs and purrs,

—Emmy Lu

CHAPTER 25

Tongue Tips

Subject: The Cat's Meow
Date: Monday, December 6
To: All My Friends • From: Henry jm

My life was simpler in the mountains. I slept, played with leaves, ate, played with more leaves and piled on my sisters to keep warm. I don't know what would have happened to me if I had been in Julian yesterday. There were more inches of something called snow than I am high. I am told that white stuff is very cold and I think I would have been buried and frozen. Instead I was in my toasty warm house.

There are so many things that happen in this thing called a house. People come and go, Dolly, the black poodle horse, is always a source for entertainment and vigilance. Things called "Christmas decorations" are in the process of being unboxed, and ever so often the doorbell rings and there is a box with MY NAME on it. It wears a boy out!

I got a special new pillow from Punkie that has a picture of me on it in something I think is called needlepoint. It is a very pretty pillow. I sleep on it. It says, "Life is uncertain, eat dessert first." I wasn't sure what any of those words meant, so I had to ask Mom. I don't know what dessert is, but I know I have only one thing in my bowl, so I'm not sure how to eat it before I eat it because some part of it might be the dessert. Mom explained that dessert is a treat, her favorite thing. I asked why I didn't have any dessert. She looked a little embarrassed. She hunted through a bag of presents for me and

there was something called Kitty Kaviar and she gave me some. It was the best thing I ever tasted! So she gave me some more. She told me that was my *dessert*. What a swell word that is. I will share my KK with all of you so you can have some before you eat your dinner. (I didn't want any dinner after that, I just wanted more KK.) I think I like this new activity; I will put it on my "make this a ritual" list, which is ever-growing.

Both my Moms have calling cards, pieces of cardboard they give to people so they know who they are or something like that. Well, I got a box of calling cards from my Aunt Heather. In the upper left corner it says, "Mood Elevation on Demand." In the center it says "HENRY & DOLLY'S Property Management." And then in the low-

Henry & Dolly's
Property Management

er right it has both of my Mom's phone numbers. I have a big box with hundreds of my cards in it. It made me feel very important, as if I was going to be here a long time. Imagine me, a country cat now doing property management. Now if that isn't the cats' meow I don't know what is.

I have a question to ask all of you cat people: My Moms — dear as they are — are cat ignorant. It seems I sleep with my little tongue partly out of my mouth. They took my picture so you can see what it looks like. They don't know if that is good or bad or normal or what. Because I am the only cat I know, and because I am asleep when I am doing it, I don't know I am doing it, and I don't know what normal is. If any of you have any information for them, please let them know. I don't bite it off. I think it just likes to be aired, but what do I know? Maybe I am dreaming of dessert and wanting to make it easy for everybody to put some on my tongue. I don't know the answer, so I thought I would ask all of you.

Yesterday, all the boxes came out that were labeled "Christmas Decorations." It was a splendid day. I chewed and batted and climbed in and out of everything. I got told "No" so many times that I stopped listening. Why do people have so many colorful, splendid toys if every time you touch them or taste them you are told "No"? What on earth good are they if you can't bat them or toss them in the air or taste them? It appears these delicate beautiful things live in a dark box for most of the year. Then, when they finally are let out, I guess you are supposed to have them be visual candy. Looking at them is stimulating and it makes me want to

do something with them. My biting each thing was checking to see if these were more things called dessert. At the end of the day, all the boxes got repacked and a few things got put on the mantle, which they are not sure I can climb onto. I can't understand why those pretty balls and figures got put away. They said about each one, "Well, that's another one he'll break," and back in the box it went. Heck, it might as well be broken if it is stuck in some dark box all year. People are funny. They seem to want to just have and look at things. I know how

to turn things into a game. They had a thing called a stocking, I got in it, I heard the camera go snap and then I fell to the bottom of a very deep red hole. It was fun. I have a lot to teach my Moms. I am young, they are old, and I will win out in the end. By next year everything will be out for me to play with and every day each of the things will look a little different and be in a different place. Now, how interesting is that? Bye for now. Hugs and holiday purrs to all of you!

— Henry jm

Subject: Tongues
Date: Monday, December 6
To: Sir Henry
From: Mr. Rhett Butler

Dear Sir Henry:

This is not only normal, but sleeping with your tongue out is very cute. You deserve a special treat for that! Like, more caviar.

— Best, Mr. Rhett Butler

Date: Monday, December 6
To: Henry • From: Iris

Dear Henry's Moms:

Chill out. It's no big deal. I do it all the time. It's like one of those hereditary things, ya' know? We Julian's (that's our last name in case you didn't know) sleep like that. It facilitates the exchange of positive and negative ions and improves our brain functioning. That keeps us creative, active, and inventive in our awake time so you don't know what's gonna happen next. It also enhances the kitten's best weapon, the cuteness factor, thus maximizing our training of humans to be more highly responsive staff members.

— Sincerely yours, Iris, your sister

Date: Monday, December 6
To: Hank • From: Jamie

Hey Hank. I agree with everything you think!!

When I had my cat, somehow I also had a Christmas tree. I think it was because my cat enjoyed being outside and chasing leaves or mice or birdies or who knows what, rather than monkeying with the tree... plus I confess, I did use the plant sprayer so that the cat would not bother the tree and the ornaments, and I always put the non-breakable ones toward the bottom just in case.

But you are a lucky guy: You have Mommies to love you all day long. My cat (Hobbes) had to stay by himself lots more often, and so I think that's why he loved the outside so much…because he wasn't alone. I had to work. That money thing, ya know…. Also, Hobbsie lived outside by himself for the first year of his life. He was what they called "feral." That was a big joke, just like it was a big joke that I couldn't be tamed either. A whole bunch of great people came in my life, like they did for Hobbes the cat, and made it so the world could be safe. And predictable. Or at least reasonably sane…nobody purposely doing something to trick me just to see how nutty I might become. Wow! Am I glad THAT is all over!!!

Anyway, sweet Henry jm, and your dear Mom Cathy: Enjoy your days together. I think having your own calling card is GREAT!!! I have some, too... but they aren't as great as yours… though I bet I am as proud of mine as you are yours!! Happy Holidays!! Go PLAY!!!

— XoXo your friend, Jamie

Date: Monday, December 6
To: Aunt Jamie • From: Henry jm

Dear Aunt Jamie,

Wow, you have cards too, how great is that! I would like your cat Hobbsie, if I could meet him. I think I would still like outdoors, but it has been a long time now, I don't exactly know. I like it here and there are lots of things to do. What is a plant sprayer, and why would you use it on a kitty?

I will get them to put some more things out for me to play with, but I do have a lot of my own toys too.

I am glad my Mommies live at home with me. Mom Cathy still works, but they say there is enough money for us whether we work or not. I am a lucky little guy.

— Love, Hank (Henry jm)

Subject: Tongue Tips
Date: Monday, December 6
To: Henri • From: Auntie Mariam

Dear Henri,

Tell your mamas that some animals have tongues that are a little bit too long for their mouths, and sometimes they just let the ends hang out. Rajah has an ENORMOUSLY long tongue — longer than his snoot, which is also very long! Usually he curls it up inside his mouth, but once in a while it slips out. I think it's very cute. When Rajah licks me, I am always amazed by how long it is. It's like pink velvet, unlike yours, which is more like fine sandpaper. I wish Rajah had a sandpaper tongue — if he did, maybe he could keep himself clean, as you do with yours. One of Rajah's pug friends, Arthur, nearly always has the end of his tongue sticking out of his mouth. Pugs have almost no snoots to speak of. In fact, Arthur's Moms call him "Squish-Face" as a term of endearment.

It is raining here. You are lucky that you live with Dolly instead of Rajah, because Rajah does not have a Christmas tree, or rather, his are all outdoors. He says, if you can't pee on it, then why bother to have it in the house? He would prefer living outside with his trees to bringing them into the house. When we go out on the deck, he makes a point of peeing on the potted evergreens, just so that they know their place. Rajah and I light Hannukah candles in a pretty brass candle holder that looks like a dove of peace with spread wings. Since Hannukah is really a rather minor holiday, that's all we do, unless I get in the mood to make potato latkes. We like that it reminds us of the miracle of light during the darkest days of the year.

— Auntie Mariam

Date; Monday, December 6
To: Auntie Mariam • From: Henri

I got some very good information from a lot of my friends about my tongue. They all think it is fine to let it all hang out, and it helps me with my cute factor, which is a good card to play in a dog household. My Moms like dog kisses but not kitty kisses. They like purrs, so that will have to do. I do keep myself clean with my tongue.

We are supposed to get rain tomorrow. Now that I am an indoor cat it doesn't matter to me what is going on outside. I never peed on trees in my woods, but it is an interesting concept. I mostly just ran up them. I can't remember about my accident. Who knows, I might have fallen out of a tree. I have never seen a candle or had a latke. Maybe my Moms will show me soon. I really like my new world. I hope they want to keep me .

— Henry jm

Date: Monday, December 6
To: Henri • From: Auntie Mariam

You are so cute!! Your little pink tongue is so cute!!! I'm tempted to catnap you and bring you back to Philadelphia. Rajah would just have to deal with it!

— Love, Auntie Mariam

Date; Monday, December 6
To: Auntie Mariam • From: Henri

I take catnaps all the time, but I didn't know you could *be* catnapped. That is an interesting concept. I will have to think about it. Mom Cathy is getting to like me and she is slowly starting to stop calling me a "cute little pupper." I think, in time, I will totally win her over. Dr. Mom already adores me. I keep Mom Cathy busy being my scribe and my photographer.

— Henry jm

Subject: Cat Nappers
Date: Monday, December 6
To: Henri • From: Auntie Mariam

Well, there are catnappers and CAT-nappers, and you have to watch out for the latter kind…. I call the young of all species "puppies." My human friends think it's a little weird when I coo over their babies and talk to them as if they were Rajah's babies. But really, you can't go wrong if you raise a baby as you would a well-behaved puppy. Just feed them when they're hungry, cuddle them, play with them, and clean up their pee and poop.

— Love, Auntie Mariam

Date: Monday, December 6
To: Auntie Mariam • From: Henry jm

Thanks, that is good to know. I thought catnaps were just all good. There are many things I have to learn. I guess it is fine that they call me "she" a lot, plus a "puppy." The bottom line is that I get lots of food, cuddles, toys, and I have a black wooly horse I am trying to turn into a sister. I still have a long way to go.
  Love,

— Henry jm

Subject: The Tongue Thing
Date: Monday, December 6
To: Henry jm • From: Cheryl

Well, Henry, it does sound like you are the cat's meow. I talked to your Mom's last night at Uncle Bob's and Steve's party. You would have had a great time there with many things to play with. (They are NOT cat people, therefore it would have been problematic, and you would have made Uncle Steve's eyes turn red and blow up.) Your

Moms love you very much, and are very happy you are in their lives, and that you don't make them sneeze!

Don't worry about the tongue thing. Not only do cats do that, but my god-daughter did it too. As long as you don't bite it, it shouldn't hurt you to "let it all hang out."

Property management is a booming business for cats and dogs. Most have the run of their homes most of the time and have to share it only a few hours a day. You are lucky to be in a management position all day long.

I hope you have a very wonderful holiday season, with as much KK as you can eat. Life is short.

  Love,

— Cheryl and Kitty

Kitty in her natural state.

CHAPTER 26

Calling All Cats

Subject: Introducing Myself
Date: Tuesday, December 7
To: Henry jm • From: Thelma

Dear Henry,

My Moms are really loving seeing all your photos and hearing your news. I'll admit, grudgingly, that you are fairly cute (for a boy cat) and you write a pretty good letter, but between you and me, my Moms still tell me I'm the most beautiful girl in the whole world, so….

However, I heard them say they're awfully sorry they don't have more time or ability to write: one Mom is working at an office all day (when she's not running around the country) and the other Mom is working at home and zooming all around the city all day (when she's not running around the country, too!), so they end up not writing. But I know they REALLY like getting your messages and I have to be careful not to get my own cute nose out of joint...

I do want to tell you that I'm awfully glad your accident turned out so well-----I mean, I'm sorry, truly sorry, you lost your little leg, but you seem to be just as mobile as the rest of us (and more!) and you sure found a great home!! Congratulations, and please keep on writing.

A purr to you,

— Thelma (Mom's transcribing this for me from her office)

Enter, Thelma

Subject: Hello Thelma
Date; Tuesday, December 7
To: Thelma • From: Henry jm

Dear Thelma,

It sounds as if you landed in a home with very important parents that have to run all over the country. My parents are OPs (older people). Their idea of running around the country is putting me and Dolly into a moving machine and going up to my beloved woods. Who takes care of you and loves you when your Moms are running around the office and country? I think I like having my Moms around a lot. I have turned into a little love boy, I like to play a lot but I also like to snuggle in the blankets.

I am trying to get Dolly to play gently with me. She has really big heavy paws and I am still a little guy. I like her, I never hiss at her or arch my back, she was here first and she is my friend.

I wish my sister Iris had been happier to see me. Maybe another time. I feel really sad because Vicente's Julian cat from a year ago was found dead under a bush last week. He must have not had nine lives like me. Oliver was a good little boy and Vicente cries for him.

I heard you were the most beautiful girl in the world. My Moms call me she a lot and then start calling Dolly he and we mix up pronouns a lot in this house.

I can't even remember my accident, I hardly remember my former life. I can do everything and am so quick no one can keep up with me so I think whatever happened landed me here and here is a really nice place.

Thanks for writing.

– Henry jm

Date: Tuesday, December 7
To: Henry jm • From: Emmy Lu

Dear Henry,

My Mom has been really busy the last couple of days and it's been killing me to not be able to send you a letter. Well, tonight she finally said we could get on the computer so I can let you know I really appreciated getting your holiday pictures and letter. As far as sleeping with your little tongue out, there is nothing abnormal about that. I used to do that when I was little but I think you'll grow out of it when you get a little older. When we're little we just let everything "hang out."

How splendid that you got Kitty Kaviar. I've never heard of such a thing so I asked my Mom if we had any. She told me no but that the

next time she went to the pet store she would look for some. I'm really excited for her to go.

My Mom talked to an old, old friend of hers today and found out they are going to move to the Philippines next year. Her friend asked her if she would take her 2 cats in to live with us as she couldn't take them with her. The lady is very, very sad that she can't take her babies but she knows if they come to live here they will have a good home. Weeeelllllllll, Dad is going to have to move next year too and Mom may be going with him. If that happens then Mom is worried about how she's going to get all of us to the new home, let alone another two kitties. That would make 6 kitties and 2 dogs for a total of 8 furry people in our house! Wouldn't that be a houseful?! Well, anyway, Mom has to make a very hard decision but she will wait until Dad comes home to really see what can be done.

Mom needs to send a letter to Dad now. He hasn't heard from Mom in a couple of days cause Mom and the ladies went to see Bette Midler last night. I don't know who that is but Mom said she was a "hoot" and the show was wonderful! She and the ladies had a good time and Mom really enjoyed herself.

Take care Henry and stay inside where you are safe and warm. Your inside house can be just as fun as your outside one once you get used to it!

Purringly,

– Emmy Lu

CHAPTER 27

Busted!!!

Date: Friday, December 10
To: All My Friends • From: Henry jm

"I could have sworn the butter was right here!"

I have had the run of the house for many hours for the past day or two. Yesterday, when both my Moms were in another room I went exploring all the counters. Good smells in this kitchen. I found a dish that had a long yellow stick on it. I licked it. It tasted really good. So I licked it again and again. It was about the best tasting thing I ever laid my tongue onto. I went off to bed quite pleased with my secret evening snack.

This morning Dr. Mom asked Mom Cathy whether she left the butter out on the counter. She didn't remember but said probably she had left it out. Dr. Mom told her to go look at the butter dish and the butter. She did and there was the evidence, a groove on one end that was just about the shape of my little pink sandpaper tongue.

They tried to scold me but instead some giggles leaked out. Once I heard the word butter I remember my friend Punkie telling my Moms to let me lick some. She said that I would like it and that it would make my coat shine. I don't know about the coat but I REALLY like butter.

Before I headed for the bedroom I made a few kitchen passes but the butter was gone. I wonder where they hide it?. Mom tried to take a picture of my little tongue trail but I guess you would just have to have been there. I have lost a few of my newly found privileges, busted for the night. Tomorrow is a new day.

Good night…snuggles and purrs.

– Henry jm

Subject: Butter
Date: Friday, December 10
To: Henry • From: Iris

Henry-

What's butter?

I don't think they have that here.
Haven't found it yet. Where else do I look?

Love,

– Sis

Date: Friday, December 10
To: Henry • From: Kitty

Moms, unfortunately, get trained too. The smarter they get, the less you are going to get away with.

My Mom lets me get on the desk top, but doesn't allow me on the counters, and uses that darn squirt bottle to persuade me that I shouldn't be up there. That bad stingy thing happens from nowhere when I get up there. Anyway, they say there are dangerous things up there like hot "stovetops" (whatever that is) that if we leap onto one we can burn our little paws. I think I would protect that one paw and listen to your Moms and stay off the countertops! Maybe the butter will end up on the floor sometime, where you can enjoy it below counter level.

— Kitty

PS: Mom says I get hair in her keyboard, but she blows it out and lets me stay between her and the computer screen. She says I make a better door than a window. What could that mean?

Kitty

My Dear Nephew,

I must say, you are not doing a very good job of training your humans. They must be made to understand that anything you chance upon in the house that is edible is yours — assuming, of course, that you choose to eat it. That is one of the Ten Kitty Commandments. (There will, of course, be a lot of human food that you won't even want — humans have an inexplicable taste for food that has been dead for rather a long time.) I know — if it's not alive, how can you tell if it's really fresh? But try telling them that! Not only do they eat pre-killed food, they eat food that doesn't even have a sporting chance of getting away, like plants! I mean, how much fun can that be?? Booooring. They also have a propensity for eating rectangular and circular food, like sticks of butter and cheese balls. How can they blame you for trying to sculpt some of that clunky, square-looking food that doesn't move into more interesting shapes with your clever little tongue?

If you don't teach them these things early in life, you will have only yourself to blame if they underestimate you and take away whatever it is that they refer to as your "privileges." What on earth are privileges? And if they give them to you in the first place, why would they want to take them away? Remind them of another Kitty Commandment: Once you give a cat something, you can never, ever take it away.

I trust that the next time you write you will have more progress to report.

— Much love, Auntie Mariam

"Now [smack], __this__ is a clever tongue!"

thought you were a dog person, too. Sometimes I get really close to my Moms' mouths so I can tell what they have been eating and if they have held out on me. They do eat some strange-looking things, but I am just a youngster and I have to figure it all out. I want nothing but privileges. I want a world of no "Nos" or "Bad Kitty." I will train them. I have been here for only four weeks to the day. I still have a lot of training to do.

— Henry jm

Date: Friday, December 10
To: Henry jm • From: Emmy Lu

Henry, Henry, Henry,

You certainly do some exploring don't you? Butter, of all things! My Mom doesn't leave anything on the counters because she knows I will get up there and investigate. Sometimes she forgets and I get to explore something new before she catches me. It's great fun and I sometimes do it just to get to my Mom. She always scolds me but underneath she is giggling. Sissy gets up on the counters now too, and Mom has to get after her. She's very, very nosy and wants to be into everything. I don't think where she lived before that she had much freedom and now she just has to be everywhere. Sometimes she drives everyone nuts, but we all had to adjust when we were brought into our new home. She will probably settle down in a little while.

My Mom is giggling about your adventure with the butter, but she doesn't want me to know! But, I'm a cat! All self-respecting cats are supposed to be nosy. It's in our job description.

Love to you and your Moms.

— Emmy Lu

Subject: Re: Kitty Commandments
Date: Friday, December 10
To: Auntie Mariam • From: Henri

I like knowing some of the commandments. It sounds as if there are about eight more. My Moms are really nice, but they are a bit slow on understanding what I can get into. They seem to have the limited mentality of dog people. How do you know so much about cats? I

Henry's Auntie Mariam with her canine crew.

"We could lick Henry any day with *our* clever tongues."

It is a new day and I have lots of new trouble to get into. Tee hee!

Love,

— *Henry jm*

Subject: Advice
Date: Saturday, December 11
To: Henry jm • From: Auntie Joan

Henry,

I am glad that you can't yet figure out how to open the refrigerator door. But, if you ever do figure it out, be sure that the freezer door stays shut COMPLETELY after you leave. We heard about a VERY bad situation last year when some houseguests made a terrible mess!!! WE wouldn't want a repeat of that, and besides, your Moms keep the butter in the other side. Remember, you shouldn't eat too much of it, no matter how good it tastes, cause you don't want to elevate your cholesterol.

— Auntie Joan

Date: Saturday, December 11
To: Henry jm • From: Aunt Jamie

Date: Saturday, December 11
To: Emmy Lu • From: Henry jm

Dear Emmy Lu,

Thanks for supporting my inquisitive mind. My Moms never had to worry what was on counters. Before having the black horse poodle they had two Jack Russell terriers. They are low to the ground. It is taking my Moms a bit of time to adjust to what is out of my reach (which is nothing). Anyway, if you get a chance, I highly recommend this thing call butter, and remember my friend Punkie says it makes your coat shine.

Oh Henry jm!!! We *ARE* kindred spirits!! Ask your Moms! I hardly ever eat much sugar stuff... but boy oh boy... do I love BUTTER!! It is better than chocolate. A friend of mine (a very little friend at age 4) came out in my kitchen one day with a stick of it in her hand and said "Good cheese Jamie... good cheese!"

I agree!!

— XoXo, Jamie

CHAPTER 28

Doctor in the House

Date: Sunday, December 12
To: All My Friends • From: Henry jm

Well, I went back to my Julian woods. I don't think I like riding in cars. It is interesting for about a minute or two and then the world is just going by too fast. It makes me very squirmy. An hour and a quarter is a bit longer than I want to sit on anyone's lap.

Somehow, I ended up back at that Vet again. I don't think I want to keep going to him. The good news is they all fuss over me and say how handsome I am. The bad news is that they then gave me something that tasted bad and two pokes into me. *MeoooOW* I said, and then it was over. I am no longer so little; I have gone from 3½ pounds to 5. If you really want to know, I was really happy to leave before anything worse happened to me.

Back to my Julian house and all my wonderful familiar smells. There was a warm breeze all around me. It was wonderful! I looked everywhere, but there was no sign of my other two sisters. Their bed and igloo were gone, and so were they. I guess it is just me and Dolly. My Uncle Jim and Aunt Janet came by because they hadn't seen me since I became a tripod. I played with both of them and it was fun. After they left, I started not to feel very happy. I can't exactly explain it, but I didn't feel at all like me. I curled up in a chair in the bathroom and didn't move for 10 hours. My Moms were really surprised to see me all curled up. They got worried. I didn't budge. I didn't drink and I didn't eat even though Mom tried to tempt me

"Wake me up when I'm well."

with treats. I just stayed really still to see if the feeling of not being myself would leave.

It didn't leave. I stayed in that spot all morning. My Moms called the Vet's office and they said that feeling lousy for a day or two was not abnormal. It was for *me*. I didn't even have enough energy to chase my feathers. Mom brought in the little bear with the nurse cap that Uncles Mike and Kevin sent to watch over me. I wonder if they knew I was going to need the nurse. Long ride

"Maybe if I sleep on this I'll get a new paw for Christmas."

home and then back to bed for me. I ate a little but it made me sick. Why does a Vet take a perfectly healthy kitty, me, and give me things that make me sick? I don't understand, but I think I am done with Vets, even if they do say nice things about me.

Thank Dog there is a doctor in the house. She has tended me all day. Mom Cathy gave me a little butter. I couldn't resist that. It hasn't been a very good day for me. Mom says that I will be better tomorrow. When is tomorrow? I want to feel better now. My Aunt Barbara in Michigan sent me my own paw stocking and a neat toy leopard's tail. They say that a leopard is a VERY big cat. It looks interesting but I was not feeling up to playing with it, so I am off to bed. I fell asleep on my stocking, tomorrow I will crawl into it.

Hugs and purrrrrrs

— Henry jm

Date: Sunday, December 12
To: Henry • From: Emmy Lu

Dear Henry,

I am so sorry that you are not feeling well. It is good that you are putting on some weight. That will keep you healthy. Sometimes when you go to the Vet and get your shots it makes you feel really crummy afterward. It upsets your stomach and then all you want to do is sleep. The shots make you very, very sleepy. I don't understand why going to the Vet makes you feel crummy when it's supposed to make you feel better, but there is something in the medicine they give us that just doesn't sit right sometimes. You will be feeling much better in no time. Just keep snoozing and time will pass quickly and before you know it you will feel good as new and will have forgotten all about the vet. Then you can enjoy your new stocking and begin your adventures again.

My Mom went shopping today and finally got your "fuzzy." I got a new one, too, and it is so cool. I have been throwing it up in the air and jumping and chasing it all evening. My Mom also got you some neat little pillow things that have this stuff in them called "catnip." I don't know what that is, but I sure do know that we all like it in our house. It's a real treat when Mom brings "catnip" home. You should have your "fuzzy" soon. I hope you enjoy yours as much as I do mine.

Take care, Henry, and live each day to the fullest. You will be feeling better really soon.

Hugs and purrs,

— Emmy Lu

Date: Sunday, December 12
To: Emmy Lu • From: Henry jm

Dear Emmy Lu,

I am feeling a little better, but my tummy is not quite right, and I sleep a lot — just the way you described. I don't understand purposely making a fellow like me feel lousy. What on earth is the point? My Moms were really worried, and they petted me a lot. I think I will just snooze more, as you say.

Your Mom sounds swell. I don't need anything new. I have so much here. But, I must say, I am really excited about the fuzzy thing. It

sounds as if it is a wonderful toy. I will tell my Mom to get some catnip, that sounds wonderful, too.

I do try to make each day full.

What do you hear from your Dad? Is he in that place called Iraq? Is there anything I could do to cheer him up? I hear that people like your Dad keep me and all the rest of us free. Tell your Dad I am grateful and I hope he comes home soon to play with your "fuzzy" and all of you.

– Love Henry jm

Subject: Sissy
Date: Sunday, December 12
To: Henry • From: Emmy Lu

Dear Henry,

I'm glad you're feeling a little bit better. Your Moms are doing the right thing by just giving you lots of TLC. That's the best medicine for all of us.

My sister, Sissy, got in trouble today. She got in Mom's butter when she wasn't looking – hee hee. Guess she just got too curious when I told her you said it was sooooooo good. Anyway, when Mom turned around and saw her there she scooped her off the counter, gave her a couple of swats on the hiney and told her "NO!" Well, Sissy doesn't pay any attention to Mom anyway. She just looked at Mom as if she had lost her mind and walked away. I was taking my morning nap when it happened but I heard the commotion. I just smiled to myself 'cause Sissy is so mean sometimes I was glad she got in trouble! But none of us stay in trouble with Mom for very long, so everything was forgotten in a few minutes.

My Dad is on his way to Korea. Mom says that's way around on the other side of the world. He's OK, but he's pretty lonely for all of us. It will be nice when he gets to come home in a couple of months. I send him your letters to help cheer him up. He knows what you look like and enjoys reading your letters after a long day at work. It gets pretty boring where he is so it's always nice for him to have mail.

You'll be back to your old self in no time now.

– Cuddles, Emmy Lu

Bad, Sissy! Bad!

Date: Sunday, December 12
To: Emmy Lu • From: Henry

Dear Emmy Lu,

I am feeling a lot better today, more like my old self. I don't think I want to go back to see people in white coats that poke you. They are definitely not high on my list. I got lots of attention and that was nice.

Tee hee about Sissy. Mom says butter is good for my coat, but that eating it when I want — not when she wants — is not good. Humans have such silly rules. Why is Sissy so mean? I thought all cats were nice like us.

I don't know where Korea is but it sounds as if it is very far from you and your Mom. I will write to the President and tell him to send him home to you. If it is a boring job they probably don't really need him anyway. Why float about on a boat when you could be home snuggling with your Mom and cats? Can't he just say no? I want him to go and find a job where he can be with you guys all the time. Maybe he could chase leaves or something like that. That is not boring. That is a lot of fun.

Your Mom has a lot more important things to do than go to a post office in a busy season to send me a "fuzzy." Be kind to her. My Moms are getting older, too: Tired bones or something. Dr. Mom has so much metal in her body that her whole body lights up when she goes through the metal detector at the airport. I guess she had her whole back fused and her neck fused and got a new knee. I don't know what any of those things mean except now she can walk and she is doing a sculpture of Dolly. Maybe I will send you a picture of it. She is really good. Maybe she will make one of me. Take care of you and your Mommy.

— Love, Henry jm

Date: Sunday, December 14
To: Henry jm • From: Punkie

Henry —

Sorry you aren't feeling so good. I'm with you — I don't like riding in the car either. My Mom puts me in a box when she takes me in the car. But she never takes me to good places — it's always to that guy in the white coat that sticks sharp things in my leg or my shoulders and puts pink stuff up my nose. Awful! When I see Mom with that box, I run and hide and hope she can't find me. I don't like that guy with the white coat. He smiles and laughs at my three legs, but then he hurts me. I don't like him.

Just sleep a lot and you'll feel better. And maybe your Mom will give you some more butter, and that is always good. Groovy.

See if she'll give you a bit of chicken — that might make you feel better. My Mom gets a big cooked chicken and gives me chunks of it.

She eats the dark meat and gives us cats and the dog the white meat. It's very tasty. Whenever one of us cats is sick, Mom goes out and gets a chicken for us. On holidays she gets a chicken for us, too. Lion King likes shrimp – but me, I like chicken.

Hope you feel better tomorrow. In the meantime, just sleep. If I were there I would give you a few sandpaper licks and a cat massage.

– Love, Punkie

Date: Sunday, December 12
To: Sir Henry • From: Rhett Butler

Dear Sir Henry:

Well, I guess we are on the same schedule. Mommy took me to the doctors, and they sent in 3 big people to shave my tail so they could attach some kind of thing that squeezed it. They were afraid I would scratch them, but I just crossed my front paws and purred while Mommy tickled both chins. Then the bad part happened. They took me to a room without Mommy and stuck something in me, and funny stuff came out. Mommy said they need to check my thyroid, but I didn't care. I purred through everything. That really throws them off. Then I came home, threw up once (I hope Mommy doesn't do this too often), had some breakfast, and went to sleep. Sorry you weren't feeling well. I hope you're feeling better.

Your dear friend,

– Mr. Rhett Butler

Date: Sunday, December 12
To: Rhett Butler • From: Sir Henry

Dear Rhett,

I don't understand. Why did it take three big people? Only one was with me. Why on earth would they shave your beautiful tail? Boy,

I don't want to go to your Vet! Mine sounds better by comparison. Why would anyone squeeze your tail? Good for you for just purring. It is good not to do what people expect. What did they put in you and why did they do it? Do they want stuff to come out of you? I threw up once yesterday, too, and then went to sleep. I am still pretty sleepy. Maybe tomorrow we will both feel better.

– Love Henry jm

Date: Sunday, December 12
To: Henry jm • From: Gillie

Dear Henry,

I am taking three kinds of medicine to make me better, and they all make me sleepy and not eager to play. I know what you mean about not wanting any more Vets. Before I got my friend Cleo, I tried to make

Gillie

the yellow cat my playmate. In the warm two days this week when I was resting on the deck in the fresh air, the yellow cat came to see how I was doing, and when Cleo wanted to chase her away, the cat just told her to mind her own business that she was coming to see how I was. She walked all around me and then sat down beside me for a little while. Cleo was making very strange noises, somewhere between a howl and a growl. My Mum went to get the camera, but the yellow cat did not know that so he got up and jumped back across the fence. Cleo had to give me a bath with her tongue to make sure I was all right.

Your grateful friend,

– Gillie

Subject: It's In the Stars
Date: Sunday, December 12
To: Gillie • From: Henry jm

Dear Gillie,

There must be something in the stars. Several of my friends, including you, went to the Vet and don't feel very perky. That was really nice of the yellow cat to come and visit you. Wow, three kinds of meds, that is really a lot. No wonder you don't feel very well. If we will just sleep more today and tomorrow we will probably be better. When Dolly gives me a bath my Moms say it is so

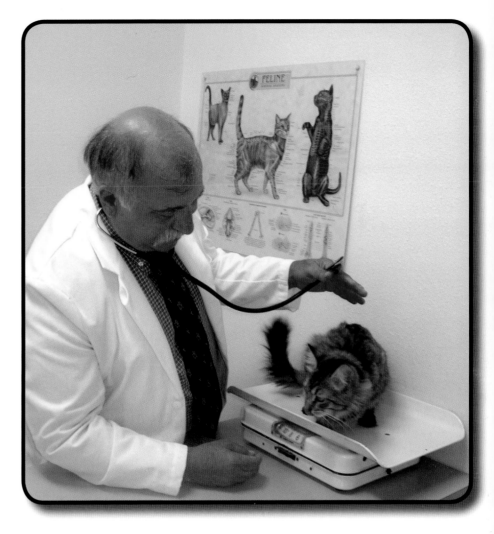

that everybody will know I belong to her. That is silly.

I am my own man. I don't belong to anyone. If it makes Dolly feel better I guess she can lick me. She seems to think that there is much too much attention going my way so she has gotten a little clingy, insisting that people pet her by pushing her head under their hands. I like Dolly. I think we will grow up to be good friends. Take care, Gillie.

– Love Henry jm

CHAPTER 29

Henry Recuperating

Date: Monday, December 13
To: Henry • From: Emmy Lu

Hi Henry,

I'm glad you're feeling much better today. Getting poked is not a fun thing but in the long run it does help to keep us healthy.

Sissy is mean sometimes, I think, because before she got to us she was an "only" and really doesn't know what it means to play nice. She's getting better, but sometimes she still slaps us with her claws out and that's not nice since the rest of us don't have ours. Mom is going to take her to the Vet to have them removed. She just hasn't set up an appointment yet. Maybe after the Christmas rush is over and things settle down a little bit.

I'm sure my Dad would love to be home chasing leaves. He loves to work outside and always keeps the yard looking really nice. Mom says it's therapy for him since he's cooped up on the ship so much. She says he can retire in a few years. Maybe I'm "retired" since I'm home all the time and I'm really happy.

Your Dr. Mom sounds like she has had lots of surgeries to fix things that were broken. I got the pictures of the sculpture. It's beautiful and looks just like Dolly. Dolly should be very proud that she now has her own statue. I'm sure Dr. Mom will make one of you too. After all, you are a very special boy and need to always be remembered.

I better go now. Loves and snuggles,

– Emmy Lu

Date: Monday, December 13
To: Emmy Lu • From: Henry

I have figured out how to put my front paw under a door and pull it open. TEE HEE, my Moms are so surprised. Dollygirl just accepts a closed door as a boundary. To me it's a challenge!

I have my claws. Mom clips them, which I don't like very much, but it is over fast. I think both of us must be retired because we are home all the time and we are happy. Retired is clearly the thing to be. I wonder why everybody doesn't do that.

I feel so much better today, I feel almost totally like myself, which is a good thing. Take good care of yourself and keep on training your Mom.

— *Love, Henry jm*

Subject: Recovery
Date: Monday, December 13
To: Punkie • From: Henry jm

Dear Punkie,

Thank Dog for Punkie II. She put her arms around me and held me all night and kept me feeling safe while I snoozed. I guess if I sleep enough I will wake up and feel like me again. My Mom did give me some butter. I really liked that. I will tell her to get some chicken today. I didn't want to eat anything yesterday and then when I ate a little, I threw up. I didn't like that.

I don't think I like the guy in the white coat either. My guy laughs, smiles just like yours, and then hurts me. Pooh on that. Every weekend we go to my original home, so that part is good. And then, two days later, I get in the car and come back to my new home. The car part is not so good.

I will just take another catnap so I can feel better quicker. Thanks for being my friend.

— *Love Henry jm*

"Soon I'll be in the pink, instead of just lying on top of it!"

Date: Monday, December 13
To: Henry jm • From: Punkie

I'm glad Punkie II is there for you to cuddle with while you sleep. Sleep is good, but it's no fun to sleep alone.

I have never thrown up, so I don't know what it feels like. But Scooter throws up all the time… several days a week. I hope I never throw up.

Mom says she uses the "chicken test" when one of us cats is sick. If we won't eat the chicken, then she knows we are REALLY sick. I've never been too sick to eat chicken, even when my leg was all mangled and Mom was

trying to save it. I had a fever and had to take medicine, and my leg was a mess, but I could still eat just fine. I hope I never get too sick to eat chicken — I'm afraid if that happens, Mom will take me to the guy in the white coat, and I definitely don't want to go there again! Take good care.

— *Love, Punkie*

Date: Monday, December 13
To: Punkie • From: Henry jm

Dear Punkie,

I had never thrown up either. And I would rather not do it again. It is very unpleasant. I have not been very hungry, but after you wrote I asked Mom for some chicken. I ate a little of that, which was really good. You are right about a lot of stuff. The thing I just go nuts for comes in a can. It is called Kitty Kaviar and it is the best thing I have ever had in my little mouth in all my born days. If you haven't had it, ask your Moms to get it.

I sleep with Punkie for part of the night. I crawl under her and she puts her big arms around me. She is very comforting. I think of you when I cuddle with her.

Take care of yourself so neither of us have to go to that guy with a white coat. He is definitely not on my list of uncles.

— *Love Henry jm*

"Oh my Dog, I can't believe my good luck!"

wonder? And why kill them? It's more fun to play with them and chase them. I'm confused.

OK, it's late. Gotta sleep.

– Love, Punkie

Subject: Mice
Date: Monday, December 13
To: Punkie • From: Henry jm

Do mesmerize your Mom. It is really worth it. You can get it at the pet store, so I am told. Poor Fannie. I think we should outlaw guys with white coats. They seem to make all of us hurt, no fun. We could form a little protest movement with the tripods at the front of the line. I don't know what a mouse is, but a lot of my friends talk about them, so they must be interesting.

I am feeling more like myself. Somehow I lost two days! I will have to make up for lost time. Take care.

– Love, Henry jm

Date: Monday, December 13
To: Henry jm • From: Punkie

I didn't know what a mouse was either, until I saw it on the front porch. Mom lets me go

out sometimes because I promise to stay very close to the house and not go beyond the fence. Fine with me. I hang out in the bushes and watch the other cats and Fannie. So I watched as Missy caught the little mousies. But once they were dead, she got bored and walked away. They must not taste very good, since neither Missy nor Fannie eat them. Me, I'm sticking with butter.

Glad you're feeling better. Yup, guys in white coats to be avoided at all costs. OK, gotta go. Time for my morning catnap.

– Love, Punkie

"This truly is elegant living. I think I'll stay. My Moms have such good taste!"

Date: Monday, December 13
To: Henry jm • From: Punkie

Hmmm, never heard of Kitty Kaviar. I'll definitely have to mesmerize Mom so she will get some for me.

Hope you're feeling better. Missy has killed three little mice in the last week, but she doesn't eat them. She just leaves them on the porch for Mom to pick up. I guess the food here is so good she doesn't want to eat the mice. But then why catch them at all, I

"Maybe I could just inhale it. Oh but then I couldn't chew it!"

Date: Monday, December 13
To: Henry • From: Kitty

Hello Mr. Henry,

I hope you are feeling better now. It is the pits to get poked at the Vets office. My Mom says that since I am an indoor kitty, she doesn't think I need all of those shots every year. They make me not feel so hot either. And they make a big bump where they jab it in my shoulder. That must have hurt your shoulder, it probably is a little sensitive anyway, if they gave it there.

Hope your beautiful stocking is filled with goodies. Christmas is a very special time.

You take good care of yourself.

– Love, Kitty

Date: Monday, December 13
To: Kitty • From: Henry jm

Dear Kitty,

I feel a whole lot better today. I am up for playing again. I don't think I will get any more of those shots. I am going to be an indoor kitty, too, so if you don't have to have them every year, why should I? I've never had a Christmas. Thanksgiving was really swell, so if it is anything like that, I am really looking forward to it.

– Love, Henry jm

Date: Monday, December 13
To: Henry jm • From: Kitty

Dear Henry,

I am so glad you are better today. Where do your Moms get Kitty Kaviar? I am going to send my purchasing agent out as soon as possible to find some for me. It sounds great.

– Love, Kitty

Kitty

"I love the fact that they named Kitty Kaviar after me."

"Now, where's my free can?"

CHAPTER 30

Back to Being Me

Date: Tuesday, December 14
To: All My Friends • From: Henry jm

Wow, I hardly knew myself since Saturday and then I woke up today and I was back being Henry, just me. What a relief. Just so all of you know, DON'T GO TO PEOPLE IN WHITE COATS THAT POKE YOU, YOU WON'T FEEL LIKE YOU ANYMORE.

Mom says I am back to being a scamp and getting into trouble. One of my friends was writing that her Dad got to retire in six years and then he would be able to chase leaves and be happy. I do all that now, so I guess I am a retired kitty. I hope you all retire; it's lots of fun.

There is one door in this house that I am not allowed out of but "Dollygirl" always goes out of. She goes out for a while and then comes back in and then the door gets shut. It is a heavy door. I cannot pull it open with my paw the way I can the other doors. So, as you might expect, that is the only door that I am interested in going out. Well, as luck would have it, I found a moment in time and I was able to get out. There are two big things in that room that look a lot like the thing that hit me and changed my life. I think they are called cars. I walked very carefully around them because I didn't know if they would move. When those things move, watch out! Then guess what I found, a little door and yes, you guessed it, it went OUTDOORS. It wasn't exactly like my outdoors in Julian, yet it had different air and smells than indoors. I ran up and down a ramp and smelled all sorts of things. Some of

it smelled like Dolly, so I guess that is where she goes when she wants to get away from me. If you really want the truth, it looked like the worlds biggest litter box. I guess dogs don't use little clean private purple places as I do. Well, it solved the mystery about where Dolly goes.

It took a bit of time for Mom to realize I was lost. Well, you see, I wasn't really lost — I was where I was. You can't be lost if you are where you are. It is true I didn't know what to call the place that I was in. I was there so I wasn't lost just because it had no name. It is hard to explain, but it made sense to me. Because I could hear Mom being frantic about "Henry being lost" I decided to come back in. Everyone calmed down. I don't think I understand at all this thing about moms having to know where I am all the time. Sometimes I don't want my whereabouts to be known, so I go where they can't see me. I guess my Moms don't understand cats yet. Dolly lies around in the middle of everything, so they always know where she is. That is no challenge or fun. I like to be sought after. Anyway, I just wanted to let you know I am well and now that I know how to get outdoors I plan to have a lot of neat adventures. I am quicker than either of my Moms, so I will find a way out.

Whoooopeee, I can hardly wait.

— *Love, Henry jm*

Date: Tuesday, December 14
To: Henry • From: Jamie

OK Henry! Don't gloat!!! Glad you had a little bit of adventure... and you didn't scare your Moms too long. Being scared for too long is horrible. If you plan to go out...don't gloat about it. Just find your way, and then find your way back home!! Promise? OK. Deal.

And BY THE WAY – I wear a white coat at my job, and I promise I never ever poke anybody and never ever would.

XoXo

— *Your friend, Jamie*

Date: Tuesday, December 14
To: I Henry • From: Puffer

Dear I,

I have a secret place I go to when I want to get away. Mom and Santhefan call it the "Do Drop Inn." When I won't or don't come when I'm supposed to, one of them says, "It must be happy hour down at the 'Do Drop Inn.'" I come back when I'm good and ready. They have NO idea where it is.

— *Puffer*

Date: Tuesday December 14
To: Puffer • From: I Henry

Hey Puffer, I have one place so far that they haven't found me in. I don't know why they always want to know where I am and if I am OK. I lived out in the woods for months and I did just fine (although it is ever so much better here).

— *I*

Date: Tuesday, December 14
To: I Henry • From: Puffer

Hey, I !

Do you have any idea how old you are?? The reason I'm asking is that you need to figure out when you will be about six months old. When you figure that you are that age, you need to find A VERY GOOD PLACE TO HIDE. YOU WILL NOT BELIEVE WHAT THEY PLAN FOR YOU!!!

— *Puffer*

"I have but one front paw to give, and I'd like to keep it."

Date: Tuesday, December 14
To: Puffer • From: I Henry

Hey Puffer,

You know how to scare a guy. I am five months old. What on earth do they have in the plans? I have already lost a leg!

— *I*

Date: Tuesday, December 14
To: I • From: Puffer

Hey, I !

Like to lick yourself? Keep yourself clean? Enjoy that? It's going to take LESS time after next month. (You ain't lost nuthin' yet!!)

All I know is that when I got discovered here, I was with my two brothers. When we were six months old we all went on one of those "this is for your own good" trips to the Vet. When we got back and got our lives back in order, my two brothers were missing some parts. I had a scar, but I couldn't see that anything was missing. Must be different for male cats and female cats.

Don't think about it. Won't do any good either way. Those "this is for your own good" trips aren't much "good" as far as I can tell, especially for male kitties because they KNOW what's missing.

— Puffer

Subject: Naughty Kitty
Date: Tuesday, December 14
To: Henry jm • From: Kitty

Oh Henry, you naughty, naughty kitty! It is not nice to panic your Moms, you know. As long as you are not lost and not in danger, that is what is important. There are things called coyotes where I live that would make us a tasty morsel if they had a chance. You also need to watch out for big birds. A hawk or an owl will take kitties like us for a ride that we won't like the ending of.

P.S. You look so handsome with the striping on your face. Is that permanent makeup? I would like to get some of that. It looks really good on you.

You take care. Glad you are back to being you.

— XOXOX, Kitty

Date: Tuesday, December 14
To: Henry jm • From: Emmy Lu

Dear Henry,

See, I told you that you would get better. I'm so glad to hear that you're back to being a scamp. I guess that must be what they call boy kitties 'cause my Mom just calls me a stinker. I think maybe I'd rather be called a scamp. Mom knows all my hiding places and knows when I'm having an adventure in the garage (even though she forgets me out there sometimes. She always comes to rescue me at some point, though. Sometimes I think she forgets me on purpose just to "teach me a lesson," whatever that means, but Mom forgets that I am much more stubborn than she is.

I got up in the window this morning hoping to find a fly to chase, but there weren't any. Guess because it's so cold outside they must be sleeping and don't come in the house. It's no fun when I can't find one to chase. I haven't seen a spider in a while either, so my hunting skills are getting rusty. I can hardly wait until the weather gets warm again and all the hunting can resume.

I'm certainly glad that you are feeling up to your old self. Keep on with your adventures but always remember to keep yourself safe. Happy holidays to you and your Moms.

— Snuggles, Emmy Lu

Subject: Don't Gloat!
Date: Tuesday December 14
To: Henry jm • From: Jamie

Oh sweet Henry jm!! I am grinning from ear-to-ear while re-reading your note. I say "Don't gloat" because I *know* you know how to live in the woods…. Anyway, another reason I say "don't gloat" is because your Moms are people — not animals — and they don't know all you know. They truly don't know that you love them, and that you know where you live, and will keep coming back no matter what. And they are really good moms. So it's a good idea to help them out and not worry them.

But I am guessing that you won't worry them for long — and I "get it" *that you want them not to worry at all!! You are such a great guy. I love all your fuzzy little fur and whiskers. I love it most that you help your Mom Cathy write. It's good for her, for you, and for all of us!*

XoXo

— Jamie

Subject: Thanks, Jamie
Date: Tuesday, December 14
To: Jamie • From: Henry jm

Are you sure you were not a cat in a former life? You seem to get it a lot. I will try not to worry my Moms. There is talk that tomorrow I may be brought out to the yard and let run. I am really excited about that prospect, but we will see if it happens. My Mom has a bunch of braces on her right hand and arm, something about tennis elbow, makes it hard for her to type and really hard to throw the ball for "Dollygirl." I think Dolly should exercise herself. I do. Vicente wants to give me a bath, I don't think I will like that, and besides I am very clean. After all, I am not a dog. Thanks for loving me.

— Henry jm

Subject: Exercise
Date: Tuesday, December 14
To: I • From: Puffer

Dear I,

When your MAMAs go to the store, do they get paper or plastic? Have them get paper. Paper sacks were invented just for cats. They are a wonderful

invention. MAMAs usually empty the sacks on their own, but do NOT allow them to fold up the sacks and put them away. Knock one over. Get inside. MAMAs have an immediate urge to scritchy scratch on the outside of the sack. Pounce on that spot. MAMAs enjoy this and will scritchy scratch in a DIFFERENT spot. Pounce on that.

This is a very kind thing for you to do for your MAMAs. They need exercise, anyway, and bending over and scritchy scratching is GREAT exercise for them. Do this OVER AND OVER until you get bored with it. Go to sleep inside the sack. Your MAMAs will probably need to rest by then anyway!

— Puffer

CHAPTER 31

So Close, Yet So Far

Subject: So Close Yet So Far
Date: Thursday, December 16
To: All My Friends • From: Henry jm

Well, there has been a very big discussion between my two Moms as to whether I should be allowed to go out into the big yard that I can see. The plan was to have three grown ups go with me. Can you imagine three big people keeping track of one five-pound three-legged kitty? It makes me giggle just to think of it. My two Moms almost always agree, but they don't on my outdoor outings. Dr. Mom says no, I will run away and they will lose me. Mom Cathy says where is he going to run, there will be three of us and he likes it here. So far, Dr. Mom has won. She doesn't want me to get lost. I have tried to mesmerize her into understanding that I won't wander away, I will stay close by — and just because they don't know where I am doesn't mean I'm lost. So far, I have gone from a completely outdoor kitty to a totally in-house kitty.

Well, Mom Cathy felt bad for me and wanted me to have an adventure. She held me and gave me an elevator ride down the steps into this magical place called her office. There were so many things to explore, so many shiny reflections on the walls and wonderful places to crawl up onto and under. I went everywhere in the three rooms and had a grand time. Then she took me into what is called the sculpture studio. That was really swell. I found something that moved in the sink and I played with it a lot. Mom said it was a spider. After I played with it a while it must not have wanted to play anymore because it stopped moving. I guessed it wanted to nap, so

I went exploring other places. I found a great big thing wrapped in plastic. It looked about the same size as Dolly. When I climbed up on it, it looked just like Dolly. Mom said it was a sculpture of Dolly. It is really nice. I hope she makes one of me. Everybody who lives here has a sculpture of them. I live here now so I want one too. Maybe when Dr. Mom finishes Dolly I can be next.

I looked out and saw all the trees but every time I went to go out my nose went bump against something hard and cold. I used to see trees and then climb them. Something has changed.

Anyway, it was a pretty good day. It is OK with me if you all vote about whether I should have supervised visits to the garden. You probably know my vote. I will send you pictures of all the neat stuff I saw. I can't send you a picture of the spider because he is asleep.

— Love, Henry jm

Date: Thursday, December 16
To: I Henry • From: Puffer

Dear I,

How does Dolly vote on your going outside? I bet SHE could find you if you hid somewhere or misplaced yourself accidentally. As smart as your MAMAS are, they would be no match for a cat determined to have an adventure. Dolly WOULD be.

— Puffer.

Date: Thursday, December 16
To: Puffer • From: I Henry

Dear Puffer,

I don't think I could rely on "Dollygirl." I think she would be sort of OK if I went and had an adventure and decided to live with someone else. I think she likes me OK but Mom says she is jealous and has become more insistent on pats and affection since I came. I wouldn't trust her making sure I stayed home. She might open the gate.

— I

Subject: Dawgs
Date: Thursday, December 16
To: I Henry • From: Puffer

Dear I,

Pokey hates my guts but she knows where I am . She knows what tree I am in or which bush I am hiding under. All Mom has to do is follow Pokey to find me. Mom says, "Where's Puffer ?" and that spotted snitch finds me with great delight. Pokey knows she is not allowed to hurt me but she LOVES being the one who thwarts my plans. She puts her polka dotted nose to the ground and off she goes. She thinks being told she is a "Good Girl" is a reward. Go figure that one !

— Puffer

live with someone who hated my guts and loves to thwart me. How come you don't mesmerize Pokey the way you do your Mom?

— I

Date: Thursday, December 16
To: I Henry • From: Puffer

Pokey suffers from unabashed exuberance. She'd NEVER sit still long enough to be mesmerized. Mom did well to convince her that she must NOT hassle me. I think that is one reason she loves to snitch on me. She was ASKED to conspire against me.

An additional thought: Dogs want to please. Dogs want to be obedient. They even have "obedience schools" for dogs ! Can you believe that ? NO ONE has ever suggested an "obedience school" for cats!! HAH!! Fat chance.

Even if Dolly does not appreciate the contribution you have made to your MAMAS, she will STILL try to please them by finding you EVEN IF IT IS NOT IN HER BEST INTEREST TO DO SO.

— *Puffer*

Date: Thursday, December 16
To: Henry jm • From: Emmy Lu

Dear Henry,

I am in agreement with Dr. Mom on the fact that you should stay indoors, at least until you are a little older and have a little more meat on your bones. Then, if you still insist on going outside, you should have supervision. You are very smart and since you are also very curious you may just slip away to somewhere that isn't safe for you and then your Moms would feel terrible.

Jut because you know where you are doesn't necessarily mean that

Date: Thursday, December 16
To: Puffer • From: I Henry

Wow, I wonder if Dolly would do that? Dolly likes me, we cuddle and touch noses a lot. I just don't think she likes that I seem to be the new kid on the block and get a lot of attention. She gets wild when she plays, that's when Mom is scared she will hurt me. I wouldn't want to you're not lost! And besides, you got to have a cool adventure in your Mom's office as a consolation prize. What a neat place. I go in my Mom's office all the time. When I was littler I used to play with the mouse on the computer. But now that I'm bigger it doesn't intrigue me as much.

Enjoy your "kittie-dom." Exploring is the best thing we cats can do. Hooray for finding your first spider! Aren't they fun. You will eventually realize that when they don't want to play anymore, it's probably because you've mashed it.

Sorry, Henry, but I'm afraid I have to vote against you're going outside right now. You will get so used to staying inside that after awhile you won't even want to go out even if you're given the chance. Trust me, I know.

Happy spider hunting!

– Snuggles, Emmy Lu

Subject: Re: So Close Yet So Far
Date: Thursday, December 16
To: Henry • From: Punkie

Yes, I understand how moms worry. And it's no fun for them if they are stressed all the time worrying about you outside. You can have a fine life as an inside cat, so whatever they decide will be good. But I have a hunch that you are an EscapeO Cat…given how

you broke out of your compound ... so even if you are an indoor cat, I bet you will sneak out whenever you get a chance!

But be considerate of your Moms – it's not fair to make them worry all the time.
          – Bye for now, Punkie

CHAPTER 32

The Bath :(

Date: Friday, December 17
To: All My Friends • From: Henry jm

I just couldn't believe what happened to me today. I was walking along, playing with a light beam, and my friend Vicenta came and picked me up and put me in a gray, hard, square thing in the kitchen. I think it is called a sink. Well, I didn't know what it was, and I love Vicenta, so I just stayed there and purred. That is, until this really shocking thing happened. For no reason at all I was squirted with water from all over. In an instant I was soaking wet. I didn't know why, and I didn't want to be there, and I couldn't believe what my good friend was doing to me.

Well, it didn't stop there: The next I know, Vicenta put some stuff on me and rubbed it all over my body. There were bubbles and all sorts of troubling odors and sensations. I tried to slither away, but Vicenta had a solid hold on me. I was so horrified that I couldn't even howl or *meoooow*. How could this be happening to me and why? One minute I was chasing a light beam and the next minute I was being drowned. I didn't like it but it was over pretty quick. Next thing I know I am wrapped in a multicolored towel and am being brushed and rubbed. That felt a lot better than the bath. It took me a long time to get back to what I was before I was thrown into that grey sink. When I was dry I guess I looked handsome and smelled like people want me to or something strange like that. Don't get me wrong, I really like

The very face of feline funk.

it here and I really like my Moms, but this bath thing is a one-time deal. They got to try it, and that is it. I know how to keep myself clean. I am not "Dollygirl." I am not allowed to go play on the ball field like she does each day. Heck, I am an indoor kitty, how dirty can an indoor kitty get? I think they felt so bad for me that maybe they will never do that again. At times it is tough being a kitty in a home that has 131 years of dog experience only. Lucky I love them or I'd be gone. We all have a learning curve and they are stretching theirs. I wasn't going to tell you but I thought you should know. What was even worse is my Mom, who runs around with that shiny thing that flashes, stood there and made flashes at me so I think there are pictures of me in my pathetic state. She might even send them to you but I hope not. Somehow, I think I lost a bit of my dignity, or maybe it was them who lost it. Somebody lost it so now I have to go and find it. Have a good weekend.

– Henry jm

"Wet, yes – but wiser."

"Oh boy, if I had just one more paw...."

Date: Friday, December 17
To: Henry jm • From: Punkie

Henry —

Oh my gosh! How terrible! Why did they do that to you? Were you bad? Were they punishing you?

Oh, how awful. I have never had a bath, but a couple of the cats here have – but only in desperate circumstances. One cat messed with a skunk and got skunk juice all over her, so she had to have two baths – one with tomato juice and one with soap and water. I wasn't around then, but she told me about it on Halloween when we cats stayed up late telling each other horror stories. I shuddered to hear her story and now I shudder again to hear yours .... and it's not even Halloween!

I hope I never have to have a bath. Tell your Moms that cats don't need baths unless some-thing awful, like a skunk or a ton of mud, happens to them. We are great at cleaning ourselves...and we will even clean other cats if they are our friends. I would be happy to come down to your house and give you a cat bath, if I could figure out some way to get there without having to go in the car. Lion King gives Scooter baths all the time – especially his face and head, which is harder for a guy to clean himself. Lion King licks my head sometimes, too. He is a really good guy – big and gentle and he seems to take each new-comer cat under his guidance until we know the ropes around here. It's good to have a guy like him around.

I'm glad you felt you could share your terrible story with me and the rest of your friends. As my Mom says, "that which is shareable is bearable."

– Extra love today, Punkie

Date: Friday, December 17
To: Punkie • From: Henry

Dear Punkie,

I have gotten so much sympathy for that horrible event that my Moms won't be doing that again. Anyway, I have almost forgotten it and got such nice sympathy and reinforcement from my friends it was almost worth it. My Moms are new at this and they are allowed a few strikes before they are out. That was a big one. Maybe it should be counted as two. They thought it would cut down on dander or something like that. What do they know! They are dog people. It is true, once I told my story I felt better. Take care, no more baths.

— *Love, Henry jm*

Date: Friday, December 17
To: Henry • From: Emmy Lu

Dear Henry,

EGAD! A BATH! WHAT WERE THEY THINKING?! We indoor kitties don't need baths. How could they do that?! If your Moms feel like they need to groom you or something all they need to do is brush you on a regular basis. You can and will keep yourself perfectly clean so there is no need to drown you in the sink. I am mortified! If my Mom ever tried to do that to me I would never speak to her again. Of course, my Mom has had cats all her life and knows

better. Your Moms mean well though so don't be too upset. Maybe they won't do it again. I'll keep my paws crossed for you.

Keep in mind that you are training "dog" people to learn how to be "cat" people too. It may take awhile, but at least they always mean well and you are very loved. Being loved erases the shocks of being bathed and of going to the people in white coats and being poked. Actually, being loved makes all the bad things better. I know, 'cause my Mom loves all of us and we are all very spoiled, well cared for, and healthy.

Keep yourself clean, Henry. Then they won't be so tempted to bathe you again.

— *Kitty kisses, Emmy Lu*

Date: Friday, December 17
To: Emmy Lu • From: Henry

I think they learned their lesson. All my friends were aghast. I don't think they thought I was dirty, I think they thought it would cut down on dander, whatever that is. They brush me and clip the tips of my nails. I sulked for an hour but I really like them and they are just dog people and they are older and have to be taught. They said (at least one of them said) that they won't do that again unless I got into something really horrible. Now what, I ask you, could be more horrible than a bath? Go figure. I think they just are new to the kitty

thing. I am a pretty forgiving kitty and I owe them more than one for saving me.

Take care, Kisses and purrs,

— *Henry jm*

Date: Friday, December 17
To: Henry • From: Sister Iris

HENRY-

OH MY GAWD, THIS IS TERRIBLE. WHAT ARE THESE PEOPLE THINKING??

You don't need a bath, water all over you. Yuck. Just what do they think you are doing all day when you are licking your fur and grooming yourself. You gotta throw 'em a hairball. Then they'll know what a clean boy you are and you definitely do not need water to be clean.

— *Yours in cleanliness and neatness, Iris*

Date: Friday, December 17
To: Henry • From: Kitty

Henry,

You poor dear soul. You looked like a drowned rat in that sink. Tell your Mom's that Kitties bathe themselves and are very private about that sort of stuff. You can certainly take care of your own grooming and such.

How did that awful event come about? I have never had one, in my 13 years.

— *Love, Kitty*

Date: Friday, December 17
To: Henri • From: Auntie Mariam

Dear Nephew,

I am glad that you are feeling better, but I was very upset when I learned that you had permitted your humans to give you a (shudder) bath. You must make it clear to them that kitties know how to wash themselves — indeed, they are a lot cleaner than most humans. A BATH! My word, don't let it get around the neighborhood or you will be a laughingstock!

Many human houses have large litter boxes in front and/or in back — not that humans have the slightest idea what to do with them. They go out into their litter boxes, plant and dig up flowers, and then when nature calls, they run back into the house and perch atop a porcelain bowl! All I can say is, how silly! Then some of them (you're not going to believe this, Henry) actually go to stores and buy animal poop to put in the ground around their flowers! Humans…they're a little dense, but you've gotta love 'em.

And speaking of humans, I wish they would get it that cats sometimes feel like doing cat things. You just can't do certain cat things with people around. It's all very well to play with feathers and toys, but nothing beats stalking a live mouse or a cricket, or snoozing in a spot of sun. I mean, if feathers float their boat, it's fine with me, but give me a real bird any day of the week. You won't hear me telling them to stop acting like humans — why can't they return the favor? I guess they can't like us as we really are, but only when they pretend we are furry little humans. Repeat after me, Henry: I am not a Hobbit.

And by the way, I am never lost. Just because a human doesn't know where I am doesn't mean I don't know where I am. (A human couldn't smell her way out of a paper bag, but any self-respecting cat can). Lassie isn't the only quadruped who can find her way home from

And now the nightmares!

1,000 miles away, but frankly, it's not worth the trouble to prove it.

Be well, nephew, and don't get discouraged. Humans are slow learners, but some of them eventually can become almost catlike.

Much Love,

— Auntie Mariam

CHAPTER 33

Sniffing My Way Out

Date: Saturday, December 18
To: Auntie Mariam • From: Henri

Dear Auntie Mariam,

I am trying to be patient with my Moms because they are just learning about kitties and I am new as a teacher. I won't tell anyone on the block about my bath as I don't want to be the laughing stock of the neighborhood. I do smell very sweet, and my fur is a bit softer and shinier. But I will run and hide if anyone tries to do that again.

That story about humans was too funny. I wondered why my Moms go and sit on that bowl in that room but I didn't know that they went and bought poop to put on their flowers. That is beyond belief for me. Maybe you just heard a story about that and it is not really true.

I want to be a kitty. I don't want to be a human. I will work with my Moms and show them your letter as my lobbyist for not getting a bath ever again unless I fall in a tar pit. Tee hee tee hee – the idea of buying poop is really something!

Dr Mom is the one who says I can't go outdoors. She says it is a really big house with mice in it and I can entertain myself in a safe way here. Mom Cathy doesn't agree, but is scared that if she lets me out and something happens she will feel terrible. I hope they work it out.

The yard looks like a really nice place to be. Thought you might like the pictures of me smelling my way out of a bag. The bag is way more fun than the present.

— *Henry jm*

Subject: Mousies
Date: Saturday, December 18
To: Henri • From: Auntie Mariam

Dear Henry,

You'll be pleased to know that your Auntie caught a mouse tonight. Since Aunties aren't as quick as kitties, I had to use a trap: I put it right next to the place near the stove where I found some mousie poop this afternoon. (It looked like grains of brown rice, and since I had been cooking brown rice, I didn't notice it at first.) My mice seem to like Rajah's food, so I took a piece of kibble and stuck it to the trap with peanut butter and, later, when I was restringing a necklace up in the living room, I heard a loud SNAP. I said a prayer for the mousie to speed its way to mousie heaven (sniff). To tell the truth, Henry, I don't much like to trap mice. I'd rather play with them. I have tenants, though, who jump on chairs and yell "EEEEK" when they see a mouse, so I have to convince my mice that the neighbors have fewer traps and better cuisine.

Henry, I wish you could come for a visit — I'm sure the mice would decide to go to Florida for the winter if they took one look at you. Of course, since you just had a bath and probably don't smell like a nice clean kitty at the moment, they might think you were a large, stinky bar of soap. They would be wrong, though, wouldn't they! Tell your Moms that the only water kitties like is drinking water, and that it's more fun if it's coming out of a tap, because you can play with it while you drink it. I have a friend who turns on the tap to give her kitty a drink. Her kitty once jumped up on the sink while I was brushing my teeth — I was quite startled. That reminds me of another kitty commandment: If it moves, it's more fun than if it doesn't move. Some kitties will even chase laser lights around a room. You should get your Moms to try that some time.

— Much love, Auntie Mariam

Date: Saturday, December 18
To: Auntie Mariam • From: Henri

I can't believe it: My human aunt caught a mouse before I did! That is really something. I don't know about traps, but I caught my first spider. It was a lot of fun until it decided to take a nap. Did your mouse take a nap? Why do people get on chairs and yell *eeeek* for a mouse instead of playing with it? People are nice, but they are also different. They need lessons about nature and living and letting live and playing and all that stuff. Maybe your neighbors will like to play with the mice. If you send them here I would play with them. I think the mice would like me. We could have fun. I think I am thirsty and will go ask my Moms to turn on the tap. On the other paw, that is the place I got dunked — right at that faucet! Maybe I'll just take a drink from my bowl and call it a day.

I chase fun lights all the time in the house. My Moms have a lot of things that make light move in the house. This is a really nice house for a guy like me. If I can't be an outdoor kitty, this is not bad.

My Moms just got a call that there are 70 mile-an-hour winds in my mountain home. I heard them say that I would have been blown away if I were there. I am glad I am here.

Good night, and leave the mice to me.

Love, your nephew,

— Henry jm

Date: Sunday, December 19
To: Henri • From: Auntie Mariam

Dear Henri,

As of this morning, the score is Auntie 2, mice 0. I wouldn't go so far as to say that the mice "decided" to take a nap, but let us both hope that they woke up in mousie heaven, where one can enjoy lip-smacking treats of kibble and peanut butter without risk of, er, a sudden bonk on the head. I do hope my neighbors take a more charitable view of mice.

I am sure that you look very handsome, but most cats prefer eau de kitty to shampoo or soap. Rajah has scent glands in his paws, so that when he paws the earth after he pees or poops, everyone will know exactly who did it. I love that special paw smell — a nice whiff of it is almost as good as the smell of brownies baking in the oven. You must try to sniff Dolly's paws while she is sleeping. If people had any sense at all, they would make soap that smells like paws.

Much love,

— Auntie M.

CHAPTER 34

The Taste of Freedom

Date: Wednesday, December 22
To: All My Friends • From: Henry jm

Well, I have had a lot of fun tasting flower decorations, running wild, having Dolly get told she is a bad girl when she pounces on me or corners me, playing with ribbons and wrapping paper and running to the front door to see the postman. It is a lot of work for a little guy like me. Oh, by the way, I am not so little. I am growing. One of these days Dolly will be really surprised that I got big overnight. Then we will see who pounces on whom.

There was a moment when my vigilante Moms were not on top of their game. I ran down the stairs and, as luck would have it, the shop door was open and the outside door out of the shop was open. There I was: in the FORBIDDEN GARDEN. Mom was talking to someone about the new gate being installed (I like it a lot) and out I scooted. I ran through two plants and there I was, right at the top of a running stream. It was really neat. I was just taking it all in, all the sniffs and sights and next thing I know, swoosh, I was in my Mom's arms (not a totally bad place to be). I was soon whisked back into the house. I pressed my nose against the pretty new gate, as I really wanted to go back. There *will* be another day, but that was it for today.

Then good fortune came again. The garage door was left open, so out I went. After exploring that new space I found a game with the big silver machine. I climbed on the big black round thing (Mom calls it a tire) and ran all around it. It is fun and dark when you get to the top of it. It was quite a few minutes before anyone realized I was gone, and then, once again, I was scooped up and taken back on the other side of the door.

It is interesting. There are lots of things to explore in my house, but as soon as there is a door that I am "not allowed" to go out of, it is ever so much more interesting. I wonder if that is JUST ME or if that is how others feel.

There are so many colorful things around the house. There are also good smells and I have gotten special treats. I think I like this thing called holidays. Send me some good vibes. Soon I might get out and really explore my yard. Time to go snooze and get ready for the next adventure.

– Love, Henry jm

To: Henry • From: Fran

Oh Henry,

There has gotta be a way to convince your Moms that outdoors and other wonderful places will be all right for you – in little bits of time and under watchful eyes. We enjoy your letters. Secretary seems to convey your ideas quite adequately. You are fortunate to have such excellent employees. A bonus would be appropriate I think. Take care of them, they are a fine family for you.

– Fran

To: Henry • From: Puffer

Dear I,

Remember when I asked you how long until you were six months old and remember what I said might happen to you ? (You said you didn't want to think about it ??) I won't spell it out because your MAMAs might figure it out….

Well, between us, the URGE to escape, visit, or have adventures is REALLY "cut short" by having you-know-what done. Sigh….

Don't say I didn't warn you !

– Puffer

To: Puffer • From: Henry

Puffer,

Hmmmmmm, I think I will go play with some tissue paper. I am not sure I want to think about this.

– I

To: Henry • From: Puffer

I,

Think about it, indeed! Good plan! It's called "tom catting" around. (You have MANY cousins name "Tom," incidentally, AND they "spray" things in their spare time! An ugly ugly UGLY thing to do and not much admired by MAMAs or anyone else.)

You have a good thing going for you; try NOT to screw it up. See if you can find the story of Puss in Boots and have a MAMA read it to you. He had LOTS of adventures.

– Puffer

THE GREAT GATE

Why does he like flower arranging?

CHAPTER 35

Merry Christmas

Date: Friday, December 24
To: All My Friends
From: Henry jm

Twas the night before Christmas
And all through the house,
Henry was hunting
To get his first mouse.

Dolly was tired
So to bed she was put
Henry was prowling
And not under foot.

He'd written his letters
To all his new friends
Telling them tales
From beginning to end.

Now was the moment
To make his big catch
To surprise his new Moms
With what he could fetch.

He hunted and hunted
Without any luck
The mice were too clever
From him they did duck.

He thought and he thought
What was he to do?
He wanted a present
From him to those two.

His Moms were so special
They gave him a house
The least he could do
Was to give them a mouse.

When none did appear
He went to plan two
It seemed, after all
What else could he do?

Because love and purring
Were all that he knew
Into the bedroom
On three legs he flew

With one great big leap
He was right on the bed
He snuggled real close
To be near both their heads

He purred and he whispered
In both of their ears,
Merry Christmas dear Moms
Please keep me for years.

My 2004 Christmas Poem

I'll be a good kitty
And bring you much joy
Now just you remember
I am now YOUR boy.

We'll learn lots together
With all our new friends
You write my stories
and I will press "Send."

Tonight it's enough
To lie here by your side
Tomorrow new antics
And places to hide.

To all my new friends
I wish you the best
Your friendship is special
And that is no jest.

As I go off to snooze
Know you'll be in my dreams
Your love and your letters
Are what Christmas means

And so now as I take
Myself out of sight:
Merry Christmas to all
And to all a good night

– Henry jm, Dolly, and their Moms

"And Dolly wonders why I'm not coming out!"

CHAPTER 36

The Rain and Other Gloomy Things

Date: Sunday, December 27
To: Henry jm • From: Emmy Lu

Dear Henry,

My Mom got a really nice surprise for Christmas. My Dad got to call her from Hong Kong! She wasn't even expecting a phone call so she said it was really nice to hear his voice. Christmas is over now and we all survived. I think my Dad was probably more lonely than my Mom because he didn't have anyone to share Christmas with, but my Mom had all of us. He said he was doing OK, though, and he was eager to come home.

Sometimes when Mom gets the stuff out of the box she says yuk, another bill' and other times she says "Yay, we got a letter from Dad." I don't ever get anything so I really don't worry about it too much. Sometimes I keep a watch out the windows during the day and I see him come in his big white truck. Watching all the cars go by our house is interesting sometimes. Other times there's nothing to see and it's pretty boring. I keep watching anyway – I'm really not sure what I'm waiting for. Maybe I'm waiting to see my Dad come home from work again. Then it gets all noisy around here and the dogs act silly.

I just watch coolly from my perch in the window. After all, I'm a very sophisticated kitty and I have more manners than they do.

Your Moms are learning very quickly that you and Dolly can do just fine being left alone together. We animals have built in instincts

that your Moms are just learning about. The older you get, the less they will probably worry. Probably when your Moms are gone Dolly sleeps anyway and you probably do too. That's what all of us do when Mom leaves us to go to work. We know she'll be back and then we will all get talked to and petted again. We always like it when Mom comes back home. The house doesn't seem so empty.

I hope you all had a wonderful Christmas and that the new year will bring you much happiness. By this time next year your Moms will be wondering how they ever got along without you in the first place. I'm sure you're the best thing in the world for them.

You and Dolly keep your Moms safe and let them know you love them every day. Purring and snuggling from you and licks from Dolly are the most precious gifts you can give them.

Have a happy kitty New Year!

– Snuggles and kitty kisses, Emmy Lu

Dear Emmy Lu,

How swell that your Dad got to talk to your Mom and all of you. Did you give him your best **meow** and all the other things that we know how to do? It is hard to be far away from home and the people you love. I don't even like to be alone for a few hours any more. I hear that is unusual for a cat. I wouldn't know.

Maybe pretty soon you will get something, so you better watch for the postman.

Mom is still worried about Dolly hurting me. Sometimes she does get a little rough, but I can slither away usually.

My Moms hardly ever leave home. I hear they didn't go anywhere for almost six years because Dr. Mom had so many surgeries. Well, just my luck, they go away twice in two weeks! They are going to something called the Rose Bowl Parade, so Aunt Sue will be spending the night with me and Dolly, and then we are "on our own" for the rest of the day.

I am no longer an outdoor kitty. I would get cold and hungry. I like to stay in with my toys and Moms.

I guess I will go play my evening game of mouse.

Take care.

— Love, Henry jm

Dear Henry,

Not all cats like to be alone. I miss my Mom when she's gone, so I just sleep a lot. I think the others really don't pay any attention. So I guess you and I are more alike than the others.

I'm so glad you got found and that you are now an indoor kitty. When you're an indoor kitty you always have good food and shelter and there's always lots of loves to go around. I'm glad I'm an indoor

kitty and that my Mom rescued me. I hope my sisters found as good a home as I did. My Mom would have taken all three of us but she was afraid that Dad might have a "cow." I didn't know humans could have cows, but my Mom and Dad have them sometimes — at least that's what they say.

I will watch for the postman more closely now. I am excited to see what your favorite thing to play with is. I haven't lost my new fuzzie yet, and neither have the others, so I have great fun throwing it in the air and chasing it around the room. I live a great life and want for nothing.

— Snuggles and kisses, Emmy Lu

Dear Emmy Lu,

I will give you a hint, one of the things is for you to eat, the other is for your mother to build. Bet you can't guess what it is! Hope the postman hurries; he's not as fast as you and I are. It is very blustery here. We are supposed to have a big storm. I wonder what Dolly will do? She doesn't like the rain and she doesn't use a litter box. Hmmmmmm, guess I will find out. Talk to you later.

— Love, Henry jm

Dear Henry,

You know how curious we kitties are. Now you've really got me excited! My dogs don't like the bad weather either, and sometimes Mom has to trick them to go outside and potty. None of us around here like storms — maybe yours will go right by and you won't be bothered. We'll think positive thoughts and try to make the storm go away.

It has been very cold and foggy up here. It's supposed to start raining tomorrow and for the next few days. I'm staying on my big comfy

moms. Lucky me. I haven't found another spider again, but I will and I plan to find me a fly. Mom says this is really unusual weather for San Diego. I wouldn't know, it is all new to me. I have such fun chasing feathers and my fuzzy, this is a very good life. I think I won the lottery of homes! Even if they never liked cats before, they like me.

Take care.

— *Hugs and purrs, Henry jm*

To: Henry • From: Emmy Lu

Dear Henry,

I'm glad you're all snuggly and warm in your house also. I wouldn't want you to be outside and blow away. Maybe the storm won't last too long, and then Dolly won't have to be tricked into going outside.

I got my package today! Yummy, yummy, yummy! I love my "kaviar." I'm sharing with the others and they love it too. Mom is just giving us little bits at a time so we won't spoil our appetites for our regular stuff.

Mom says thank you for her "project." How did you know that she loves to do things like that? She has always liked doing things with her hands, and used to do ceramics years ago. Then, for some reason, she just couldn't find the time anymore so now she just works on her baskets and satisfies her creative side that way. She's eager to start on her project, though, and may do that this weekend.

Mom just found out today that she has cancer, but they don't know what kind yet. She had to go to the hospital for a biopsy on a lump in her neck. She feels fine, but is kind of scared, but I know she'll be alright.

couch and will get down only once in awhile to go talk to Mom. I'll be glad when the weather gets warm and the flies come back so I have something to chase again. Found any spiders lately?

Stay safe,

— *Love, Emmy Lu*

To: Emmy Lu • From: Henry

Emmy Lu,

Boy, am I ever glad that I am an indoor cat. It is pouring rain with 40-miles-per-hour winds, I would be blown away and very cold. Instead I am all curled up with my fuzzy, toys, dog, and two

Fran and Midge will look out for her until my Dad gets home. We don't know yet whether we will have to get him home earlier than when the ship is supposed to return. It's all happening so fast it's overwhelming and Mom's brain is spinning with all kinds of things. My brothers and sisters and I will also take very good care of her. We love her very much.

Thanks again for the yummies and Mom's project. We appreciate your gifts.

– Love to all, Emmy Lu

To: Emmy Lu • From: Henry

Dear Emmy Lu,

I am glad that you got your package and that you think the "Kaviar" is as yummy as I do. I just love it and I am a pretty picky eater. You are a very good kitty to share with your other friends.

I was hoping your Mom would like the project. When it is done it works and the kitties move and then you will like it. Dr. Mom loves projects and working with her hands. I hope she does a sculpture of me someday. That is when I will know that I have permanent status here.

Me and my Moms are worried about your Mom. No matter if things are big or little they are always easier when you are surrounded by people you love. I don't know what cancer is but I have heard that people get scared if they have it. A lot of Moms' friends are cancer survivors, so I guess that means they get to stay with their beloved four legged creatures.

I think it is a wonderful idea that your Dad comes home. Tell the people on the ship that your Mom needs him more than they do and they should send him home to make her feel safe and to play in the leaves. My Moms have wonderful healing tapes and have worked a lot with people who are sick. Dr. Mom is good with medical stuff because she is a surgeon. Mom Cathy's strong suit is dealing with people's fears and emotions because she is a psychotherapist. Everybody says they are a great team. They told me to tell you that if there is anyway they can be helpful to let them know. A lot of times doctors will send reports only to other doctors. Our friends give Dr. Mom's fax number and they then get their reports sooner. Dr. Mom always talks to them a long time and explains things to them.

If you would like some treats for your Mom, my Moms are good at finding such things. You have to tell us what your Mom likes.

I think it's a wonderful idea that your Dad might come home. Snuggle up to your Mom a lot. We furry creatures are the best fur nurses around. Take care. It is still raining here.

– Love Henry jm

CHAPTER 37

Almost New Year

Date: December 31
To: All My Friends • From: Henry jm

Well, I have been such a busy boy since Christmas. I have new toys, but, frankly, what I like best is all the bags and wrapping. I jump in and out of them and it drives Dolly nuts. She pounces on them, but I have already left and am on to the next bag. I love flying from bar stool to bar stool. There are eight of them and Dolly doesn't know how to fly.

I have gotten out into Dolly's side-yard five times in the past week. My Moms start scurrying around, "Where's Henry, where's Henry?" They are so silly, I am just exploring. One of my favorite places to hide is on top of a big black round thing they call a tire. It has interesting smells on it so I climb all around it when I escape. It is only for a few minutes before my Moms come and scoop me up. *Zap*, I am back in the house.

My Moms say they have never seen such crazy windy rainy weather. They said if I had been in Julian I would have been blown away. I see pieces of trees much bigger than I am flying by, so I guess I am really glad I am an indoor kitty (at least most of the time tee, hee). Dolly was stubborn and didn't want to go out in the rain. I don't blame her but she doesn't know how to use a litter box, so Mom made her go out.

Yesterday Mom went to play with Dolly in the dark and rain in a little alley across the street. The only way Dolly would go out is if she got to chase her ball. Mom has a great big plastic garbage can

filled with Dolly's outdoor toys. Well, she and Dolly played in the rain and dark for about 20 minutes only 25 feet from the truck, which she left part-way open. She came back and there were no Dolly toys. Everything in the back had been stolen. Mom was upset and Dolly looked puzzled. I guess someone else needed some toys for their pet more than Dolly did. A lot of the toys Dolly had "found" in the past two years, on walks, in canyons, at the ball field.

For some reason Mom said it scared her and she didn't feel very safe because she was out there alone with Dolly. I told her not to be scared, Dolly and I would take care of her and some other person had dogs that really needed a bunch of toys and cable jumpers to make their car go. I told Mom that I was Dolly's new toy and we would be just fine because we have so many things to play with. Mom grumbled that that wasn't the point and said something silly like feeling violated.

I danced around and cheered her up and soon it was forgotten.Dolly had a collection of about 50 baseballs and a hundred tennis balls and soccer balls. Mom used to call her a little thief. Dust to dust and thief to thief. Mom says we had way too many toys, anyway. Dolly still has another stash downstairs. Dolly once found a cell phone on the ball field. Mom called the number on it, which made it ring in her pocket. Phone and owner were reunited. Mom says we all have too much stuff anyway and it was good that we have fewer toys. I think she is right. All we need is a paper bag and tissues. Dolly already "found" two tennis balls so I expect she will have a new collection to donate to the next thief. People are funny: They collect stuff, they store it, clean it, move it around and then — *poof* — one day it is gone. There are plenty of leaves, and that is all people need.

Well, it has been quite a year. The biggest event for me was the day I was born. Now that is really cool. I got to be a mountain cat for four months, and that was great fun. I lost a paw, which wasn't so much fun, but I don't really remember that now. I found new Moms, two great homes, a dog of my very own, and a whole bunch of wonderful new friends that have made me feel so welcomed into the world. I hope that you all had as good a year as I did. My Moms are going to something called a Rose Bowl Parade tomorrow, so Aunt Sue will be staying with Dolly and me. If there is a ball in the parade I should go, I could chase it and entertain everybody. My Moms and I wish all of you a very happy new year. Some of my new friends have Moms who are sick and going to have surgeries. Please send them all the love that you have sent me so they can heal and fly just like me.

I will tell you more of my adventures next year.

— *Your friend, Henry jm*

Date: December 31 • To: Henry • From: Uncle Bob

Dear Nephew:

Thank you for the terrific photos of you and Dolly. Just think, it was only a short time ago when you knew her only as that "big black horse," or something like that. Just shows that friendships can get deeper and deeper. This happens to some people as well, like your Moms, your Aunt Joanie, and me.

Your writing continues to demonstrate meticulous observation (those are all good words) of the human and animal worlds.

We Are Family Two

We have guests in our house now — Isabel and Joseph from Santa Barbara — and we expect to have a lovely dinner here on New Year's Eve and even perhaps stay awake until 11:30 or so.

Tell your Moms that we miss them and admire them. . . .

— Uncle Bob (UB)

Date: December 31 • To: Henry • From: Puffer

Happy New Year, I!

It is rainy and very windy up here at the Ranch. Mom says we haven't had this much rain in ten years. The word seems to be: Rain, good; Wind, bad. Usually I split my time between being inside and outside. Lucky for me that Mom lets me inside whenever I want. This drives Pokey nuts so LOTS of times, even if I don't really care, I choose "inside" just to irritate Pokey. I am SO pleased you are driving Dolly nuts. It IS the cat thing to do.

Pokey would NEVER let anyone take something that belonged to Mom. Maybe Pokey needs to send some hints to Dolly about how to be a "dawg." Pokey can be a well behaved "dog" or, when the occasion demands it, a "dawg." Pokey can be pretty scary when she has chosen the "dawg" mode. Even I do NOT mess with her when her Catahoula side is showing. She is VERY protective. Most of the time she is convinced the world's ills could be solved with slurpy kisses. Then, there are those "other" times when she would willingly annihilate something or someone she perceived as a threat and she doesn't care what size it is. (She was all for taking on the neighbor's bull that got out of where it belonged and wanted to come through our yard to get to where it wanted to go.)

Lots of new adventures are ahead for you! Enjoy!!
  Your friend,

— Puffer

Date: December 31 • To: Henry • From: Rhett Butler

Henry,

Thank you so much for your gifts this week! I have been so lonely, as I have to spend most of my time in the office alone, as my Mommies are only allowed to visit for a few minutes at a time, until I am better. They have a sign on the door that says "radioactive cat, do not enter." I have never been on the radio, but I was active when I was younger. I just don't know what is happening. Mom fed me the kitty treat you sent, and it was wonderful! She also played string with me, but I didn't play too much as I still am a little under the weather.

Mom says she won't be home this afternoon, as a brain doctor is sending her to some kind of machine to look inside. I hope it wasn't where they sent me!

Rose Bowl Kitty float

• 134 •

Tomorrow night is something called a New Year. Humans wear funny hats, and blow things, and try to stay up. I am just going to eat the caviar you sent, and keep resting.

— Your Friend, Mr. Rhett Butler

Date: December 31
To: Henry • From: Emmy Lu

Dear Henry,

You are such a dear boy! You aren't the only one who is glad you were born this year and found such a wonderful home. It's so nice to have a kitty-pal that I can write to. I never knew it would be so much fun writing to another kitty. You are very lucky to have so many new friends.

I can fly, too. I fly down the hall and over the furniture. It's great fun! Mom giggles when I do that. My dogs don't bother me much anymore now. They're really used to me cause I'm very old now (I will be 2 years old this month). That makes me very worldly and I know everything that is going on in my world at all times — even when I'm cat-napping. Lilah, the big dog, used to try and put her paw on me when I was littler, but Mom would always stop her. She was afraid I'd get squished, but all Lilah wanted to do was give me a bath. She's a very motherly doggy. Maybe that's what Dolly is trying to do to you. She probably would just like to give you

a bath sometimes. They would never hurt us, though; they just don't know that we have littler bones than they do.

I'm sorry that Dolly's toys got stolen. I can understand that your Moms are upset and feel violated. What a horrible thing for someone to do. Keep them safe and be a good watch-kitty.

Thanks for always sending us pictures of you. It is so fun seeing the things you get into. You are quite the busy one, that's for sure.

My Mom is feeling much better today — almost like her old self. She was able to take a nice shower and wash her hair (she wasn't supposed to do that after they made the cut on her), and then she put her jewelry back on. She said it made her feel normal again. She's absolutely anal about being clean. Now she just has to wait to see what the doctor's tell her this week as far as what kind of treatment she will need. She's trying to get my Dad home real soon but that all takes time. She says the government doesn't move too quickly sometimes so she just has to wait and see what happens. We hope to know something this coming week. Mom says she appreciates your

prayers cause she can use all the prayers she can get. I don't understand prayers but she says they can do miracles sometimes. If that's what it takes then I hope my Mom has a miracle 'cause I want her to be around for me for a long, long time.

Mom wants to go lay down for a little bit so I need to go lay with her. I'm being a very good fur nurse and I will keep her nice and warm.

I hope this year is as wonderful for you as the last one was. I'm sure it will be. You can't miss with two such great Moms and a dog of your very own.

Your kitty-pal,

— Emmy Lu

The Aviator
(or Henry Barishnicat)

Date: Monday, January 17
To: All My Friends • From: Henry jm

I try to be a good boy most of the time and avoid frightening my Moms, as they are older people. I never hiss, spit, bite, or claw Dolly, even though she sorely tests my patience at times. I do go on wild runs for at least an hour a day and everybody gets out of my way.

We have a neighbor across the street that had never met me. Mom brought me to the door to meet him, I was being held firmly (translate squeezed tightly) so as to be presented at the door. The man's wife had something on a leash that looked similar to a fox I had seen in my mountain home. I have since learned that it is something called a Welsh Corgi dog. I looked down from my squished perch against my mother's chest and just knew it was BIG TROUBLE. No time for any warning, no time to give that animal time to get a look at me, there was no time for anything but ACTION! I hissed loudly, then screamed and flew from the front door all the way to the kitchen. It was quite a flight, fueled by sheer adrenalin. I didn't exactly have time to see where it was I was flying, no time for an advance ticket. I assumed that wherever it was it would be better than anywhere near that foxy-looking animal. I came down for a hard landing, *thump*, but quickly scampered out of sight. My heart was pounding, but I guess nowhere near as much as my Mom's heart. They came running after me to see if I was OK. I was a bit shaken up, but I was fine. I heard them wonder out loud about whether or not I might have lost a front leg in some foolish stunt like that. I honestly don't remember what happened to me in my accident of fate that brought me to my home. Maybe I will be up for an Oscar for my aviation skills. I must be at least as good as that guy in the movies.

I must say, although I don't like being frightened, I do rather like flying. It makes a guy like me forget I have any handicap. It is a level playing field when you are in the air. If there are no paws on the ground, it hardly matters if you have three or four. I saw on a big screen in the bedroom some people flying through the air; I think I heard my Moms call it ballet. I think I may become a ballet dancer when I grow up. I do like being airborne!

I have to go practice my leaps now. Do have a nice day.

— *Your friend, Henry jm*

To: Henry • From: Auntie Mariam

Dear Nephew,

I see that like many of your ancestors (oops, I almost used the F-word, foreBEARS), you are gifted in the arts. You should know that your family tree includes not only the Great Barishnicat and the immortal Nijinskat, but the revered opera singer Maria Catlas. Beverly Windowsills is also a distant relation. And did you know that William Shakescat added 1,600 separate and distinct MEOWS to the Catlish language?

You have much to be proud of, and you have certainly earned the right to feel superior to Welsh Corgis, an inferior and tiresomely yappy breed that would have sunk into well-deserved oblivion were it not for the patronage of the indescribably tacky British royal family. I have heard, nephew, that Queen Elizabeth's butler brings her Weet-abix to the breakfast table in tupperware. When she has had her fill, she feeds the crumbs of this sawdusty snack to her Corgis. No wonder they have no manners! Humans — especially royal ones — are supposed to set a good example to other species. I do not have great hopes for this Corgi breed — after all, the heir to the British throne has stated unequivocally that he would rather be a tampon than assume his royal duties.

Continue to practice your leaps and pirouettes, and remember that human dancers have to make do with only two legs.

— *Fondly, Auntie Mariam*

To: Henry • From: Punkie

Henry,

We have a lot in common, we just move through the world in slightly different ways.

Yes … you fly … I scoot. But we both seem to get wherever we need to get to. :-)

— *Punkie*

To: Henry • From: Kitty

Henry,

You're a very talented, acrobatic cat. You, no doubt, would have taken the Oscar, if anyone would have had a camera rolling to catch your stunt in mid air, so to speak.

You take care, watch out for foxes on leashes — they can be very dangerous, I hear.

Glad you are OK.

I have a new job: paperweight. I sit on the stack of papers on my Mom's desk and keep them from moving around or being looked at. It is a very important job, and I do it very well.

Love,

— *Kitty*

"Barishnicat, indeed! Look how much higher I can jump. Plus I catch, fetch, and even reverse course in the middle of my stride!"
                                                                — *Dolly*

"I think we should change that word 'catch' because it has a 'cat' in it, and cats can't catch!"

rrrrrrrrRRRR!
"Whoa! What a ball!"

This is catch as cats can't!

"Yawn! This is just too easy, Mommy. (I do love it, though!)"

Found My Marbles!
(Lost My Balls)

Date: January 24
To: All My Friends • From: Henry jm

My Moms have a really nice game on the counter. I don't know exactly how you play it or anything, it just looks sort of interesting. I have been eyeing it from the third floor of my condo in the living room.

Last night when my Moms went to sleep I decided that I would go and investigate all the balls in this game. They are very pretty and multi-colored and sit on a wooden circle. I pushed one with my paw and surprise, it started to go around the circle and made a nice and interesting noise. Well, I liked that a lot so I decided to try it with another and then another and then pretty soon I was right in the middle of this event. Balls were going around in circles and I was batting them as fast as they came at me. Then, I don't know exactly why, but they started falling off the wooden circle. Plunk! One fell on the floor and made a big thud. Then another and then another fell. They fell on the carpet, but soon rolled over to the hardwood floor. When I batted them there they rolled really fast so I ran just as fast. It was a lot of fun to chase these big marbles in the dark.

It was fun until it wasn't dark. Mom came running into the kitchen wondering what all the commotion was about. She looked at me and told me I was a bad kitty. I had no idea what she was talking about, so I kept rolling the balls around. Next thing I knew I was being sprayed in the face. Every time I went up to the marble I got squirted. I don't like being squirted, so I stopped playing with the marbles. Mom picked them all up and put them back in their boring static places and went back to bed. A few minutes later I decided it was time to play again. Mom, now up to my tricks, came in really fast and squirted me again. I jumped down, waited until she left, and made another pass at the game. Squirt, squirt, she went. I think she was hiding around the corner. The next thing I know, Mom has a great big towel like the one that was wrapped around me after my dreadful bath. Then I couldn't see or play with the balls anymore. Now, I ask you, why does someone leave a game out if they don't want you to play with it? There, on the counter, is this really beautiful game of many crystal balls with a bath towel over it. People are really silly, but I love them anyway. Mom thinks I won't play again with the balls, but I think she is wrong. What's a boy to do?

— Henry jm

"I'm having a ball!"

"So why do they think
I've lost my marbles?"

ALL MIXED UP!

Alphabet Soup

Date: Saturday, March 5
To: All My Friends • From: Henry jm

My Moms bring out a big board with a bag of wooden tiles and sit at the dining room table. I've sat atop the bar stool and watched them have long periods of silence, and then one of them carefully picks up one wooden piece at a time and puts it on the board. Then they shake up a yellow bag with a very fun-looking red drawstring and take some more wooden pieces out of the bag. They say things like "Good Word!" or "Wow, you got a seven-letter one!" This seems very boring to me. They seem to enjoy it and spend hours at the table. For months now I have been very patient with this slow-moving ritual they call a "game." I marvel at how neither of them seems to want to bite the bag, or throw it in the air, or pounce on the whole board making the little wood pieces dance in the air. No, not my Moms. They just sit there and stare at their tiles and slowly put them down on the board.

Yesterday I was being, once again, a patient and polite boy watching this game. The phone rang and one of my Moms answered it; the other went to the bathroom. Now was my chance to show them what real fun was. I jumped on the table and surveyed all the words and then went after that nice little pouch that they shake up. I was having such fun spilling all the wood tiles that Dolly got up and joined the game. Upon their return they giggled and half-heartedly told me I was a "bad boy," but then out came that flashing thing and there I was — caught in the act.

I wonder if my Moms are the only ones who play this very sedentary game with wooden tiles? I don't know if this is a human thing or just an older-person thing. My Moms are OPs, so maybe it's just their thing.

Anyway, I made it a lot more fun, and once I had messed up their boring words they had a better time making words about me and Dolly and our house. If you have some spare time, come on over and we can throw wooden tiles around and shake up the yellow bag. I'll share; playing is always more fun with others.

The other night they left the game on the table. I had such a

good time. It took me a while to open the bag. I emptied it and then started to play. The floor was a much bigger and better place to swish around the tiles, so I flipped them on the floor. I was so proud of myself. Both Moms awoke to find "alphabet soup" on the floor. They are not entirely sure if they found all the wooden tiles. They didn't seem terribly pleased with my creativity, but I had a swell time. Why do humans have games if everyone is not supposed to play? And why not spread a good thing out? Guess I will go take a nap and dream about all those brown tiles clicking on a nice hard wood floor.

— Henry jm

Date: Saturday March 5
To: Henry • From: Auntie Mariam

Dear Nephew,

You just happen to have put your paw on the main reason why humans imagine themselves to be superior to other animals! Once upon a time, when sensible animals like cats were honing their hunting skills, some humans lay around the cave and starting naming things. Around the same time — because in winter they had a lot of time on their paws — they started doodling on the walls of their caves. Then some of these stay-at-home humans got the idea that these drawings could be arranged in lines to tell stories. After many moons passed, another human got the strange notion of drawing pictures of sounds. Eventually, somebody made a list of all the sounds humans knew how to draw, and called it an "alphabet."

Here's how the alphabet worked: A human could look at a drawing of some sounds, and know that the person who wrote it was thinking "MEOW." Pretty silly, huh? I mean, if you're thinking "MEOW," why not just say it, instead of drawing a picture? Well, by this time,

most humans were living in rather fancy caves and letting others hunt for them. Because they had nothing better to do, they scratched these sound pictures onto wood and stone so other people would know what they were thinking. (We cats didn't care what they were thinking, since we know that actions speak louder than words.) At any rate, with all this thinking and scratching, most humans have completely forgotten how to hunt — not to mention many other important things, like how to use a litter box, and how to lick their paws and wash themselves.

Nephew, I wish I could say that this alphabet improved the human species, but I fear that is not the case. Mind you, there is nothing actually wrong with putting "letters" on a board and making "words" with them. It's just that these "words" tend to obscure the more important things in life — earth, sky, fire, water, and wind....

And, when you're hungry, the scent of your next meal. So, by all means, teach your humans how to really play with those little wooden tiles!

— Fondly, Auntie Mariam

Date: Sunday March 6
To: Henry • From: Puffer

Dear I,

"Sedentary"??? I'm impressed, I. Wow! Is the game called Scrabble? Scrabble is a good word for other things, too. When you were scraping the tiles with your paws along on the floor, you were "scrabbling" in a more active form of their game. They have their game, you have yours.

— Puffer

THE UNEXPECTED LOSS

I Can't Believe What Happened!!!

Date: Sunday, January 9
To: All My Friends • From: Henry

Well, we missed the five inches of promised snow in Julian and my Moms were sooooo disappointed. They wanted to see white stuff fall from the air. Mom Cathy cancelled her clients so we could go up for the big storm that Uncle Jim promised. In case you don't remember, I hate riding in cars. It seems every time I go somewhere, something I don't like happens to me. My Moms put me in a big box called a kennel. It takes over an hour to get to my first home. I let them know how unhappy I was: I traded in *meow* for a scream. The amazing thing is they just kept on going. It made me madder than hops. Dolly's kennel was right next to mine, and, like a dope, she just placidly lay down and stayed quiet. I figured if we both howled they would have to do something. No such luck.

Finally, we arrived! Mom went out and filled a zillion bird feeders and I stood in my hunting pose ready to jump for a bird. Dolly wasn't sure what I was watching for, so she jumped up and put her nose on my rear end. I mean, this is a great big house, and you would think that dog could find her own perch as opposed to being fresh with me! *Hurumpff!* As a little white stuff fell, Mom and Dolly raced out for a five-minute play and a picture or two. For the next 48 hours, rain, rain, and more rain. I would like to say that I was there totally to report about the rain, but, it turns out, that is not exactly what happened to me.

My first clue that something was not right was when I couldn't find any water or food to eat after everybody went to sleep. Little did I know that I wasn't supposed to have any because I was going to get " fixed" whatever that means. Now, you all have been with me from the beginning. Do you think I was broken? I didn't. I always heard if it's not broken, don't fix it. I kept meowing that I was not broken, no need to fix me. It didn't exactly work. I was taken to the man in the white coat's office. Once again, everybody was really, really glad to see me. They played with me, weighed me (I am now five and a half pounds), and told me how cute I was. But I have heard all of that before, and then something happens that I don't very much like. Pooh on flattery!

No one would believe that I wasn't broken, so they poked me and – zap – I was taking a nap. I don't know how long I napped, but when I awoke I felt very wobbly. I couldn't exactly walk in a straight line. I was relieved to discover that I still had the three paws I had before I went to sleep. I sort of hurt, but the man in the white coat again poked me with a needle and then I stopped hurting.

My Moms came to get me. I was too sleepy to be glad to see them or even to meow about being in the car.

Dolly wanted to sniff me and cried trying to get into the bedroom. Mom put me on the floor because they were afraid I would fall off the bed. I didn't much want water or food, I just wanted to sleep. I didn't feel very good. Why do they take me on a perfectly good day when I am feeling swell and ruin my weekend like that?

The night was OK. In the morning everyone got up early, deciding there would be no snow and that it was time to head home. I decided to groom myself, and then I discovered it: Something was missing! I was licking myself and something was gone "down there" that used to be there. Darn, once again, a missing part! I am

not sure what that part was for, but I don't have it any more. As a sort of protest, I wiggled and meowed for most of the way home. Then I curled up in my favorite chair with my toys and blanky and decided to take a snooze.

I overheard my Moms say if I don't get used to riding in the car, they might leave me at home. I figured I must have not heard it right. They couldn't really think that I could be left behind, could they? What is a weekend without me? They would be so sorry. Anybody have any ideas on how to be a better car rider? I don't want to be left behind. That would be a CATastrophe.

I am going to nap now, it has been quite a 24 hours. NO MORE TRIPS TO THE MAN IN THE WHITE COAT THAT SAYS WHAT A NICE GUY I AM. Take care, tell my Moms that I am not broken and I don't need any more fixing.

– Thanks, Henry jm

To: Henry • From: Puffer

Dear I,

NOW you are ALL ready to be a good house cat! Congrats! That is ALL part of growing up and being responsible. Not TOO much is asked of you, you must admit, but there ARE a few little details that DO require adjusting. You HAVE done your part now! From here on out, you've got it made. You have done ALL the adjusting that is required. Now it is up to your MAMAs to adjust. Don't let them off the hook. And, believe me, there is NOTHING that you have left the white-jacket guy wants. You are not going back there!

Next time you go to Julian, relax. Fuss a snick just to let them know you are paying attention, but there is nothing to be gained in wearing yourself out screaming for an hour and a half. Enjoy the ride with your MAMAs and enjoy Julian, and come back home again. You like sacks, right ? Have your MAMAs get a sack-sized carrier. You'll feel more secure in a smaller space. Put your blanky IN it, and a towel OVER the top, turn it so it faces Dolly so you can see her. If she feels secure, you should too. She has been there more often than you have. If she's not upset, you shouldn't be either.

Take a nap, I, you've earned it!

— Your friend, Puffer

To: Henry • From: Auntie Mariam

Dear Nephew,

Humans are the only species that persist in fixing things that are not broken. If they didn't love you so much, give you plenty of food, a nice place to sleep, and great toys to play with, it would hardly be worth your time to put up with them. It does seem odd, though, that the things they "fix" don't work as well as they did before they weren't

broken. But let me tell you something about humans that you will find even harder to believe. Some humans, after "fixing" their animals by removing their reproductive organs, then replace the organs with surgical implants called "neuticles" – yes, more cutting, more sewing up, more pain! They hope by doing this to pretend that they were not so idiotic as to remove the parts God gave the kitty in the first place.

— Fondly, Auntie Mariam

To: Henry • From: Monkey Bones Zola

Hi Henry:

I hear you talkin' man. That same thing happened to me nineteen years ago and I still miss the missing part. But at least it doesn't hurt anymore. By the time you hear my letter you'll be feeling just fine again. Take care, buddy, and be sure to enjoy your youth. Mine is gone! However my Mom says I'm oh, so mellow these days. That's something, right?

— Love, Monkey Bones Zala

To: Henry • From: Punkie

Ohmygosh, Henry! You must stay awake around that guy in the white coat!!! Don't take naps around him! Every time you fall asleep, you wake up with something missing. Next thing you know, it might be an ear or your tail or something. Jeez.

I don't understand this "fixing" business. I got fixed too — I thought when my Mom said she was going to get me fixed that I would get my hind leg back…but nooooo. When I woke up from my nap, my

tummy had no fur on it and there was a cut there with some stitches holding it closed. Whatever was broken must have been inside, but I didn't feel like anything was broken. I wish they had given me a new leg instead. Oh well.

I know what you mean about the car. None of us cats travel in the car. We don't like it. We are all homebodies and we are quite content to let the dog go with Mom and tell us about it when they return. The dog loooooves to go in the car every chance she gets — but we cats don't. It's very disorienting and stressful. Mom tells me that some cats have been trained to like cars, but I can't imagine why they would. Cars freak me out. I cry and make a ruckus when Mom takes me in the car — and with good reason — it's always to go to the guy in the white coat — and you and I both know what a mean SOB he is, even though he pretends to be nice. Nope, no cars for me, thank you.

OK, Mom is calling and I gotta go to bed now. More later.

— Love, Punkie

EPILOGUE

All endings are incipient beginnings. Although this is the end of a book, it is just the beginning of this remarkable cat's life. Henry has continued to have many adventures. Dozens more have been written and over 1000 more e-mails collected from all over the world. Organizing them and answering Henry's mail seems to have overtaken this Mom's life. Surely other books will follow, as he has much to teach us.

Henry came to a town that had suffered devastating loss and to owners who were struggling with their own loss. Loss makes us vulnerable, and in that moment of vulnerability there is fertile ground for change. I suppose that is how this strange cat-being got into the hearts of dog-adoring people. We changed his life and he is continually changing ours.

Loss is awesome for all of us. A dear friend of mine who lost most of his life's work in the Julian fire reminded me that awe is the essence of the word *awesome*. We all need to be in awe of all that confronts us in our world and never, for a second, stop reaching out to make a difference where we can.

Stories are how we learn what our world is like and what we should be in that world. Henry's stories seek to tell you, through the eyes of an innocent being, what the world in which he has landed is like. In his innocence he points to the absurdities so present in our human world. Despite its challenges, Henry's world is real, and it is full of love.

More books, a Web site, all sorts of things are in the works. Right now, however, it seemed a big enough task just to bring you his first two months with us. Thanks for coming along on his journey so far. More to follow....

– Mom Cathy, Cat Scribe
under the ever-watchful eyes of Dr. Mom
August 2005

Now you have the second edition of *Henry's World*. His letter box (not litter box) in cyberspace has enlarged to well over 3500 letters. His books have been in *no* bookstores so that *all* of his profits could go to animals. Somehow, just as his letters found their way around the world, in three months his books have gone to people in almost all the states in America and 10 different countries. He seems to have found many who just delight in his antics and others who need hope after having suffered losses, physically and emotionally. He has become a symbol for beating the odds and being resilient in spirit. He has been able to get his book to several severely injured Marines returning from Iraq. He plans to get to many more amputees and chronically ill children. He wants to teach us all that sometimes the story we think is to be "our story" changes.

It is then *our* task to write a new story of what we want our life to be about and what our lives can become. Henry has tried to do that with all who come into his world. Don't be surprised if many people start writing about their adventures and reaching out to a wider world. That would really please this dear cat. He is a lot like his Moms, who want to spread an epidemic of health and healing. Now, dear reader, it is up to you to keep the "little cat that could" on his healing and heartwarming journey. He has added music to this edition because he loves music and he knows that it is healing for animals and people.

Who knows what 2006 will bring and where this "spirit animal" will go? I can now add "postal literary courier" to my résumé having mailed out thousands of Henry's books. Thanks for being along for the journey.

– Mom Cathy, Cat Scribe
Christmas 2005

YES!

I want to order _____ copy(ies) @ $25.00 of *Henry's World* by Cathy Conheim

Name _____

Address _____

City _____ State _____ Zip _____

Enclosed is my ☐ check or ☐ money order in the amount of $ _____

Please add $5 postage for a single book (book rate). For multiple copies, please enquire via e-mail for shipping/handling costs: cathy@breakthroughpress.com — or the address below.

Please make checks out to Cathy Conheim.

Visit Henry and buy books at www.henrysworld.org

Buy my book and help my friends!

BREAKTHROUGH PRESS
P. O. Box 135
La Jolla, California 92038

YES!

I want to order _____ copy(ies) @ $25.00 of *Henry's World* by Cathy Conheim

Name _____

Address _____

City _____ State _____ Zip _____

Enclosed is my ☐ check or ☐ money order in the amount of $ _____

Please add $5 postage for a single book (book rate). For multiple copies, please enquire via e-mail for shipping/handling costs: cathy@breakthroughpress.com — or the address below.

Please make checks out to Cathy Conheim.

Visit Henry and buy books at www.henrysworld.org

Buy my book and help my friends!

BREAKTHROUGH PRESS
P. O. Box 135
La Jolla, California 92038

YES!

I want to order _____ copy(ies) @ $25.00 of *Henry's World* by Cathy Conheim

Name _____

Address _____

City _____ State _____ Zip _____

Enclosed is my ☐ check or ☐ money order in the amount of $ _____

Please add $5 postage for a single book (book rate). For multiple copies, please enquire via e-mail for shipping/handling costs: cathy@breakthroughpress.com — or the address below.

Please make checks out to Cathy Conheim.

Visit Henry and buy books at www.henrysworld.org

Buy my book and help my friends!

BREAKTHROUGH PRESS
P. O. Box 135
La Jolla, California 92038